WHAT TIME IS IT?

By the same author

IF I OPEN MY DOOR
THROUGH OPEN WINDOWS
WHEN WE TWO WALKED
THE WINDS BLOW
A THOUSAND SUNRISES
WHILE THE CANDLE BURNS—*Devotions*
THE LARK IS IN THE SKY
SAFETY LAST—*Tales of the Pacific*
THE PRODIGAL OF THE SEVEN SEAS—*Biography*
LISTEN, CHILDREN—*Talks for Young People*
TODAY—*A Book of Devotions*
THERE'S NO PLACE LIKE HOME
STORY-TIME AGAIN—*For Children*
AS THE SUN CLIMBS—*Autobiography*
TREES UNAFRAID (*Lutterworth Press*)
SUNG IN OUR HEARTS—*Studies in the Psalms*
I TURN TO DUCKS

O Dandelion, O Dandelion,
The children still come to play,
But they hold you high, to tell the time,
And puff your crown away.

WHAT TIME IS IT?

A Book of Stories for Preachers and Teachers and Fathers and Mothers and all Friends of Boys and Girls

BY

RITA F. SNOWDEN

LONDON: THE EPWORTH PRESS

THE EPWORTH PRESS
(FRANK H. CUMBERS)
25-35 City Road, London, E.C.1

MELBOURNE CAPE TOWN
NEW YORK TORONTO

Made in Great Britain
Published in 1953

SET IN MONOTYPE BASKERVILLE AND PRINTED IN
GREAT BRITAIN BY THE CAMELOT PRESS LTD.
LONDON AND SOUTHAMPTON

Contents

What Time is It?

SOMETIMES, AMONG the green grass in the spring-time, you will come across golden-faced dandelions. They look like little suns that have fallen out of the sky.

But as the days pass, they change. And by the end of summer their stalks have grown tall and dry, and they hold up, instead of faces of gold, little round heads of silver fluff.

Then it is fun to pick them. They are called 'Dandelion Clocks'.

'What time is it?' you ask. Then you puff your cheeks and blow.

One blow means one o'clock. Two blows, before all the silvery top has gone, means two o'clock, three blows means three o'clock. Sometimes you can get up to eight o'clock, ten o'clock, even twelve o'clock.

Of course, it is a game—you can't really tell the time by silvery dandelion clocks. But it's fun.

O Dandelion, with the golden face
You look like the sun today,
As you wait in the green, green grass,
For the children who come to play!

O Dandelion, with the silvery crown,
The sun shines hot and bright,
The days go by, and the nights go by,
And now your crown is white.

O Dandelion, O Dandelion,
The children still come to play,
But they hold you high, to tell the time,
And puff your crown away.

'What time is it?'

It is good to know what the real time is—to be able to tell by the clock. But it is best to know—whatever the dandelion clocks say, or the real clocks—that it is time to be happy, time to be friendly, time to be courageous, time to be true.

The Lovely Outing

LITTLE JOEL rushed in breathless from school. 'Oh, Mother, Mother, what do you think? The Prophet Jesus has crossed the river. Somebody told Benjamin, and he told me. May we go and see Him tomorrow? They say He is healing all the sick people.'

'But you are not sick, my son,' said Joel's mother. 'But,' she added after a little pause, 'I have heard that He tells wonderful stories as well. We will see. Perhaps when tomorrow comes, we will be able to go.'

'I do hope we can,' said little Joel.

'Benjamin and his mother might like to come, too. We will see?'

The sun had hardly risen over the rim of the hills, when Joel's mother gathered with other village mothers at the well, to wait her turn with her water-pot.

'Have you heard the good news?' she asked. 'Jesus

of Nazareth, the Prophet, is in our parts? Little Joel brought the news last night, and I have been planning ever since, so that we can go and see Him. They say He is healing all the sick folk.'

'But your little Joel is not sick, is he?' asked one of the women.

'No, he is not sick,' said Rebeccah, 'but the Prophet Jesus is wonderful to healthy people as well as to the sick. They say He tells wonderful stories of God. I thought some of us mothers might go together and take the children.'

'I should certainly like to go,' said one of the women, 'if all that you say is true. But I would leave my baby at home with his grandmother.'

'Oh, I wouldn't do that,' said Rebeccah. 'It would be something for the little one to have the Prophet's blessing.'

'I will certainly take my youngest,' said another mother, as the cool water trickled into her water-pot. 'We might never get another chance. And we can start out with the little ones before it gets hot.'

'Come, let us go,' said another, 'it will be a lovely outing.'

So it was decided. And the women hastened home from the well, and told the children of their plan. Some were too little to understand, but those as big as Joel and Benjamin were full of joy.

The mothers washed and fed the very little ones, and the bigger ones washed themselves and put on their best clothes.

'Will I do?' asked Joel, dancing around his mother. 'Will I do, Mother? I have washed behind my ears and my knees. And my hair is tidy. Will I do?'

Rebeccah laughed at her little son. He was so eager.

'Where will we meet Benjamin and his mother?' he asked, 'and all the others?'

'Don't be in such a rush, son,' said Rebeccah, 'we have arranged it all. We will meet them as we go.'

At last, Joel and his mother Rebeccah set out, and the sun rose high. The air was full of sweet smells of the grasses and flowers, and the day promised to be a very happy one.

They met the other mothers and the children as they went, until there was quite a little party of them.

It was some time before they reached Jesus. And even when they saw where He was, a great crowd was about Him. Big people were bringing sick folk, and clever people were coming to ask Him questions, and His disciples were busy in and out.

The women tried to edge their way into the crowd, but it was hard to make a way.

'I told you He would be too busy with His big and important friends to be bothered with children,' said one in her disappointment. 'We will only tire the children in this crowd. Let us go home!'

'No,' said Joel's mother Rebeccah.

Just then a busy disciple friend of Jesus came by, and saw the children and the mothers.

'Are the children sick?' he asked.

'No,' said Rebeccah, 'but we brought them to see the Prophet.'

'Well, you might just as well take them home again,' he said, 'for Jesus is too busy today. Look at all this crowd!'

And Rebeccah looked at it, and her heart sank with disappointment.

But just as the tears were beginning to sting the eyes of little Joel and his friend Benjamin, there was a movement in the crowd. What was happening?

Next minute the voice of Jesus was saying, 'Let the little children come unto Me!'

And very quickly the grown-up crowd parted, and

Rebeccah and the other mothers and children went through to where Jesus was.

The big disciple fussed around all the time, saying in loud tones that Jesus was too busy to be bothered with women and children. But Jesus said, 'No! I am never too busy to bother with children. They are my little friends!' Then He took the baby ones up on His knee, and He talked to little Joel and his friend Benjamin and the others who were old enough to hear stories.

At last, as they went home, the mother who nearly didn't bring her baby said, 'I'm glad I brought my baby, after all. Jesus seems especially to love children.'

'Yes,' said Rebeccah softly, and very happily, 'and He wants us to love God as our children love us. He is the great Father of us all.'

When at last the mothers of Salem and the children got home after their walk, they were a little tired, but they knew that it had been the happiest day they had ever had.

The Little Girl who Sang to Her Cat

ONE SUNNY morning, a long time ago now, a little girl sat in the window singing to her cat. It was a large house where her grandmother lived. Little Jenny's mother had to earn her living, so she did not see her very often.

But Jenny was very happy. She loved her grandmother, and she liked the big house, especially the sunny window where she could curl up and sing to her cat. Her cat liked her singing, too. He curled up, pleased to feel the warm sunshine, and purred away contentedly.

Jenny's window was in the big city of Stockholm, in Sweden, and just up the street from where she looked out she could see the tower of St Joseph's Church.

As she sat in her window singing, she thought of the lovely countryside, and the singing of the streams and the birds. And she made her voice into a soft whisper, and said to her cat: 'I wish I could sing as beautifully as the streams and the birds.'

Presently a girl came down the street on the way to do shopping for her mistress. Her name was Johanna, and she was the servant-maid of a very important lady —Mademoiselle Lundberg. Mademoiselle Lundberg was a very famous dancer, and liked to have all sorts of pretty ribbons and laces to make herself beautiful.

'Come along, Johanna,' she said, 'Go into the street, and to the shops, and bring me some new ribbons. And go on a little farther, and buy me some scent.'

And little Johanna, who loved doing messages, put on her hat and cloak and set out.

She went to the first shop, and spent a few minutes picking out the gayest, prettiest ribbons. Then she picked up her little basket with the parcel, and went out on to the street looking for the next shop.

On her way, she had to pass some houses. And as she drew near to one very large house, she heard beautiful singing. At first she couldn't think where it came from. But at last she looked up, and there in a window above her head she saw a little girl. She sounded very happy, singing to her heart's content. And there was no one there but her cat.

Johanna had often heard great people sing when she had gone about to important places with her mistress, but she had never in all her life before heard such lovely, clear, sweet singing as she was hearing now.

She stood a long time listening and nobody guessed she was there, and she might have stood much longer had not the bell in the old tower of St Jacob's Church struck the hour.

'Oh, dear!' said Johanna. 'Is that the time? I had no idea. And I haven't finished my shopping. What will Mademoiselle say?'

She hurried on, but by now her thoughts were far away from ribbons and laces.

Just as she had feared, Mademoiselle was angry when she got back. 'Where have you been, child?' she said. 'And now you haven't done your shopping. Tell me, where have you been?'

Johanna was so excited about what she had heard that she forgot that Mademoiselle had not known where she had been.

'Oh, Mademoiselle,' she said, 'I have heard the most lovely singing. I stopped to listen, and the time just went like the wind over the garden, and was gone. It was a little girl. She was sitting in a window. I saw her high up. She didn't see me, but she was sitting there with her cat. Oh, if only you could hear her!'

'But I can't go and stand in the street,' said Mademoiselle, 'listening to little girls sing. Still, if all you say is true, I should like to hear her. You must arrange to bring her here.'

And just a week later, little Jenny Lind, with her grandmother and her mother, was brought to the house of Mademoiselle. It was a very grand house, with beautiful flowers and pictures. And to begin with they were all a little bit shy; but when Mademoiselle spoke to them kindly about beautiful singing, they weren't shy any longer.

'I want to hear you sing, Jenny,' said Mademoiselle. 'I know you sing to your cat.' And she put her arm around her, and Jenny looked up and smiled.

'Yes. I love my cat,' she said. 'And I love singing.'

Then Jenny's mother spoke up, and told how long before—when she had been only a very little girl—she had heard soldiers going by playing a bugle, and had climbed up to see them.

Jenny sang her very best for Mademoiselle, and Mademoiselle gave her a lovely present. But most lovely of all, she made her mother and her grandmother promise to take her to a great singing-teacher. Then, turning to Jenny, Mademoiselle said: 'Some day all the world will be made happier and more beautiful by your singing.'

And though her mother and grandmother had doubts, they did as they had promised.

Jenny went to a famous singing-teacher, and she worked very hard, going over her exercises many, many times, learning them until at last there was nothing more to teach her. She was ready to sing.

And when she began to sing in great halls, people came from far and near, and praised her lovely singing more even than Johanna had done. And little Jenny Lind became famous all over the world. She travelled to England and sang there, and people gathered in thousands to hear her. She travelled to America, and thousands and thousands more gathered to hear her. And everywhere she went, she brought beauty and happiness into the lives of people.

When one day they asked the secret of her beautiful singing she had her answer ready. She said: '*I sing for God!*' And that was the truth. That's why everybody loved her beautiful singing.

In the New Testament is a fine text that little Jenny Lind must have learned: It says: 'Whatsoever ye do, do all to the glory of God' (1 Corinthians 10^{31}).

Old Hendrik

ALL UP and down the land he wandered. Even the smallest children knew the old man with the fiddle and the bow. And as he drew his bow they gathered round him, and danced in a ring. One minute the music which came from the old man's heart was soft and gentle, like the tiny crocuses and the wild things that came early in the spring; next minute it was like the gay rippling laughter of a stream full of sunshine.

Nobody was more welcome in the villages than old Hendrik. His shoes were sometimes worn, and his wallet hardly ever held more than a few coins. He was satisfied to give his music, if he could find a little food to eat and a place to lie down at night. He loved to see the happiness of the little children when he drew his bow across his old fiddle. And he loved to see the smile come like sunshine across the faces of the hard-working people. Many of the people worked up in the high mountains, scratching a meagre living from the little patches of soil—for Norway is a country of mountains. But however hard their work, and however hard the winter had been, when they heard the strains of old Hendrik's fiddle they knew that the spring had come, and there was joy in their hearts. And they opened their doors and bade him welcome. And the good pastor welcomed him especially.

But one winter the cold was cruel and long. And there was famine in the land, and many folk had empty bowls when meal-times came.

Old Hendrik trudged wearily from village to village, but everywhere the story was the same. Furrows of care were upon the brows of fathers and mothers. The doors of the inns were closed, and so too were the houses of the people who before had always been ready with their welcome. Even the church was poorly attended, for in every home there were the sick. Even when he knocked at the good pastor's house, only silence answered his knocking, for the old pastor, weary with serving, was out day after day among the poor.

And evening came, and darkness, and old Hendrik wondered what he would do. And then he remembered that always—whate'er befell—there remained God's welcome that awaited a weary wayfarer in the little church.

Old Hendrik made his way there. It was silent and still, but in a strange way his heart was at peace.

In the village in which there was so much sickness and anxiety he felt that it would please God to hear a little joy. So he took up his old fiddle, and played once more the songs of spring and joy—the songs of the little baby crocuses, and the songs of the little streams as, full of sunshine, they ran down the mountainside. And then, as the night deepened and it became even colder, he lay down to sleep, his old worn cloak over his feet.

Only God knew that old Hendrik had played his last song. But in the morning, when the villagers and the old pastor came into the church, they found him dead.

And yet, in a strange way, they will tell you—if you go to any one of the villages that knew him—that the old fiddler does not seem dead. For in the spring it seems that the music he made is still in the air. And those who have hearts and ears to listen can hear it in the woods—softly in the joy of the little crocuses, joyous and bounding in the songs of the little streams. For then to all who have joy in their hearts—and kindness—God unlocks the frozen music of the world.

The King's Jester

ONCE UPON a time there was a little 'funny man'. His name was Rahere-R.A.H.E.R.E. He was the king's jester. He wore a little red suit, and little red shoes with pointed toes, and a little pointed cap with bells, and he knew a great many tricks.

Noblemen and princes and kings in their castles liked to have a little jester around to help pass the time and to keep the fun merry. They were rough old days, but Rahere enjoyed his life well enough in the Court of King Henry the First.

Then suddenly, one day, everything in the Court was changed. Even the gay heart of little Rahere was changed. The loss of the famous White Ship and the drowning of the Crown Prince brought sadness to King and courtiers alike.

In a very short time little Rahere was off to Rome on a pilgrimage. It was usual for very good people to do that in those days. Their pilgrimages sometimes took them a very long time, and were full of dangers. Little Rahere, whose heart had been full of fun, was not one to shirk a dangerous task, and at last he arrived in Rome.

But after he had been there a little while, he fell sick

in that distant city. So sick was he that he thought he was going to die. Afraid, he did what many people do when they are sick and afraid—he prayed, and he made a promise to God.

He promised that if God would only let him get better and go home again, he would do something for the sick people of his own land.

And at last, God heard his prayer, and little Rahere, by degrees, got better.

Lots of people forget their promises once they are better. But Rahere didn't. He said, 'A promise is a promise.' And he was the more eager about it when one night he had a dream in which it seemed to him that a man of great strength and straightness and beauty stood before him.

'Pray, who are you?' asked Rahere, looking up. 'Pray, tell me who you are.'

'I am Bartholomew, the Apostle of Jesus,' said the man of great strength and straightness and beauty. 'I have come to help you. For your great purpose, choose a place in London at the Smooth-field. Only ask for it, and you shall receive it; seek for it and you shall find it. Have no fears about how the work shall be done. It is my work to help you.'

When Rahere awakened, he was more than ever eager to get on with his promise. So he put on his clothes of a friar—a plain brown coat tied with a rope at the waist—and after a long time he stood again at the ante-room of the King's chamber.

At first his old Court friends did not know him. Rahere the little funny man turned serious! At first they thought it the best joke of all.

But it wasn't a joke. Now that he was fit and strong, Rahere hadn't forgotten his promise.

'I have business whereof I would speak with the King,' said Rahere. And when the King bade him draw near, he asked him for that piece of ground about which he had heard in his dream.

'The Smooth-field!' said those who stood listening. 'The little man must be mad! That flat, wet, marshy place is fit only for the horses that run there, and for the hangman's gallows that stands there. It's a terrible place!'

But little Rahere went next morning to the Smooth-field, wet and waste; and the people passing by laughed at him.

But the children who came to play on the Smooth-field liked the little man in the plain brown coat tied with a rope at the waist. He played games with them, and then he asked them for their help to gather the smooth stones that lay about. Soon the children began to tell their fathers and mothers at home what was happening at the Smooth-field, and they, too, came to help. Rahere explained his plan to all who came, and soon half the people of London, it seemed, had heard what was happening. Courtiers came to jeer, but they were so struck by the honesty of the work, and the joy of those who served in it, that they felt that they had to leave gifts of gold behind. Horse-dealers came, who held a market on the Smooth-field, and they too gave help as they could.

So the buildings rose higher and higher until at last the Smooth-field was changed altogether, and where there had been waste and wet and rubbish there rose a Church, a Priory and a Hospital—named after St Bartholomew, whom Rahere had seen in his dream.

Rahere's hospital was a plain, clean place, but to the poor, sick people it seemed like Heaven. Not only did they feel the kindness and tenderness of it, but they felt that it all belonged to God. Soon they needed more room for those who came, and Rahere had to get more stones and bricks and make it bigger.

Rahere made his promise and built his hospital a long time ago now—for he died in 1140—but his work still goes on. Today, there stands on part of the Smooth-fields, now called Smithfield, a great hospital, St Bart's—short for St Bartholomew's—the most famous hospital in all London. And nearby is the little church, part of which Rahere built himself.

And that is the story of the little 'funny man'.

Can you keep your promises? Little Rahere could. He promised to do something for the sick people, and he never forgot. He said, 'A promise is a promise!'

Helping the Preacher

LITTLE MARY ROBINSON lived in Yarm. Although Yarm is in Yorkshire, the largest county in England, Yarm itself is very small—just a market town, with a river sweeping round one end of it, and a straggling main street running through its middle.

But life is not dull for long in Yarm. And once a year —in October—when the annual fair is on, it is just full of life. People come from all parts, and roundabouts are set up for the children, and stalls for selling things, and lots of gipsy caravans come, as if by magic, and range themselves on either side of the street. And horse-dealers bring their horses, racing them very fast, yelling at them as they run with them, or driving them in low, flat carts. Others bargain about prices as the horses stand in rows or in the auction mart.

At night the gipsies make little fires close to their caravans on the cobble-stones of the street, and sit around the glowing embers in family groups. Some of the old gipsy women smoke pipes, and the gipsy dogs lurch around, and there is a good smell of cooking onions and wood smoke in the air. Some of the gipsies tell fortunes, and Yarm is all very full of life and interest.

On the second day, cattle are sold on the grass verge of the road just outside the town. And farmers come in from far and near to see them, to buy, or to learn how prices are going. And it is all a very busy scene.

On the third day, sheep are sold in and out of the town, and people come to see them.

Yarm Fair has also earned fame for its cheese. In one year three hundred and eighty-three wagons and carts full of cheese—each holding a ton and a half—came lumbering in to Yarm Fair. But not so much comes there today to be sold and put on a ship and sent down the river to London. But when little Mary Robinson lived in Yarm, and went to Yarm Fair, there was plenty of cheese, and still lots of people interested in cheese came and went, adding to the busy bustle of the fair.

But there were other times, too, when people came to Yarm—eleven months of the year, because the fair only happened in October. Sometimes they came to sell their farm produce, or to be fitted for new clothes, or perhaps to see their friends and relations. And sometimes they had other and more special reasons. John Wesley visited Yarm eighteen times—and his reason was none of these. Why do you think he visited Yarm? Yes, to preach.

And that was how he met little Mary Robinson. Little Mary and a little friend played one day about Mr Wesley's carriage. For a time they had great fun —pretending one minute that they were prancing, high-stepping horses, next minute climbing up into it, pretending that they were pretty ladies going on a journey. And then something rather disastrous happened—they 'put the pole of the carriage through Mr Merryweather's parlour window'. That was a sad mishap.

But Mr Wesley didn't scold little Mary Robinson and her friend too much for it. He knew what an awkward thing a carriage pole could be—besides, little Mary was still a very little girl and a very lively one. In spite of the accident with the carriage-pole, they remained good friends. And when he went in to preach, he asked Mary to help him. No, he didn't want her to give out the hymns, or to take up the collection —no, nothing like that—there are other ways of helping a preacher. He asked her if she would help him on with his cassock. Preachers don't always wear cassocks today, but in John Wesley's day they did—each wore a long close fitting black tunic under his preaching gown or surplice. And Mary helped the great preacher to get ready. She was so little that she had to stand up on a form to do it, but she did it so nicely that it was one of the happy, proud moments of her life. And when she had finished, John Wesley thanked her, and said a little prayer and asked God to bless her. And He did. And even when little Mary Robinson had grown into an old lady, she never forgot that moment when she helped the great preacher get ready to preach.

Have you ever helped the preacher get ready to preach? You can, even though he doesn't wear a cassock. I'll tell you how you can do it. You can bow your head very quietly when first you come into church, and pray a little prayer for the preacher. Then you can join in the hymns, singing them with all your heart. And when the preacher begins to preach, you can close your Bible and your hymn-book, and look into his face, following every word that he says. And when he looks down from the pulpit, and sees your eager face, and knows that you have prayed for him, and that you are listening, it will help him more than anything.

Yarm chapel is the oldest Methodist eight-sided chapel in the world, and John Wesley said it was 'by far the most elegant in England'. But the kind of church in which you worship doesn't make a scrap of difference. Wherever you live, you can still help the preacher get ready to preach, and that is really one of the most important things in the world.

The Doctor's Knobbly Bag

ONCE UPON a time there was a kind doctor, called Dr Ernest by all the boys and girls—and to them he was the most special doctor in the world. His real long name was Dr Ernest Ofenheim. He came to England from Vienna, in the beautiful country of Austria, to St John's Hospital in London. St John's Hospital was a very little hospital at that time—with only thirty beds, room enough for thirty sick people. But by degrees it grew and grew and grew. And it was a very happy place to be in if you were sick.

Dr Ernest—perhaps we had better call him by his full and proper name, Dr Ernest Ofenheim—got to love the hospital and to love the sick people. And he got to love the boys and girls especially. He loved them so much that he wanted nothing so much in the whole world as to be allowed to stay at the hospital and help.

He didn't even want any money—he could do with what he had—he wanted only to help. No wonder everybody loved him.

And he stayed at St John's Hospital helping all he could for twenty-five years, which is a very long time. And because the sick people loved him and felt safe when he was about, they soon got better. Always he had such kind hands and such a kind heart.

And there was one special thing that he did for the boys and girls that showed that he was a special kind of doctor. Every week a bag was brought to the hospital. I'm sure you'd never, never guess what was in it. Every doctor carries a bag, but this wasn't an ordinary doctor's bag: it was a knobbly bag. And it only appeared once a week. I'd better tell you what was inside it—because I'm sure you'd never guess. It was full of pennies—every one of them bright and new and shining! And, more surprising, there were always enough to go right round—so that every sick boy and girl got a bright, new, shining penny.

It was wonderful to see the Sunday smiles come creeping out when the pennies appeared—more bright and shining even than the pennies themselves out of the doctor's knobbly bag. And the smiles lasted long enough to help some of the very sick boys and girls feel better.

It was such a lovely idea that the doctor, whom everybody loved, kept it up till the end of his life—and when at last he died, he left a fund so that Sunday by Sunday bright, new, shining pennies could still be given to the sick children.

Wasn't it a lovely idea? That was *the doctor's Sunday gift*—every Sunday a bag full of pennies.

But wonderful as that was, *the doctor's everyday gift* was just as wonderful—perhaps more wonderful. For his everyday gift was kindness and love and knowledge and care—all things that help to make the world bright and beautiful.

His Sunday gift wouldn't have been half so good without his everyday gift—just as his everyday gift wouldn't have been half so good without his Sunday gift—his knobbly bag full of bright, shining pennies.

Now, you have a Sunday gift that you give: you give it to God to help His Church, and His missionaries, and His little boys and girls who haven't nice homes of their own—and you put it in the collection-plate in church when it comes round.

But what is your everyday gift? For a Sunday gift without an everyday gift isn't any good. What your loving heart does to help God's Church where you are, and his boys and girls where you are, that is your everyday gift. And it's a lovely gift—that with your Sunday gift, will bring happiness to God and help to make His world happier and happier.

Once, a hymn-writer made a little hymn about this, and in one of the verses he put this:

King of Glory, King of Peace,
I will love Thee. . . .
Sev'n whole days, not one in seven,
I will praise Thee.

The Beautiful Windows

HAVE YOU ever seen a city in your dreams—a city great and tall and white? I have. And not long ago I went on a visit to a city like that—the tallest city in the world. And it wasn't a dream. I know, because

I got a crick in my neck looking up at all the tall buildings.

In the mornings they had their tall heads in the clouds, but when the sun came out they were beautiful. And at night, when the lights twinkled from them, they looked like a fairy city. The very tallest building—the tallest in the world—is the Empire State Building in that city of New York. And there are others nearly as tall.

But the one I fell in love with was not the tallest—but one of the most beautiful. It is a church called Riverside Church. It stands by a great river. It is quite a distance from the tallest building, but when you go up the church tower, you can look from one to the other. It is a very beautiful tower—square at the bottom and tapering towards the top. And it has a lift from the bottom almost to the top—four hundred feet above the ground.

In the tall, beautiful tower—reaching up and up above the church—there is a Sunday-school and lots of class-rooms, and a nursery for the babies to play in during church time, and club-rooms for the older boys and girls, and studies for the ministers who work and preach in the beautiful church, and a chapel, and a theatre, and lots of other rooms where things happen. And right at the top there are seventy-two bells. And they ring out when it is time to come to church—and at other special times—and the people hear them a long way off.

Over the doorway of the beautiful church is a figure of Jesus, the Lord and Master of the Church, and of all those who come to work and worship.

Inside the beautiful church skilled workmen have chosen the very best wood and stone, and with loving hearts and hands have worked to make there figures and designs to the glory of Jesus.

And above where the people sit there are beautiful windows—tall, tall windows of ancient blue glass like the starry night—and all made into story-pictures that the light can shine through. In between, are twinkling parts of the story-pictures in reds and golds and greens—the most beautiful colours you can ever imagine. And if it is not church time, with the bells ringing out, you can go—treading softly—from one to another, and look at them all. They are so many, and so beautiful.

And there is one special one—special to the boys and girls, because they helped to put it there.

When the church was being built, the time came to choose the story-pictures to be worked into the beautiful windows. The big people of the church thought about it. Then they thought it would be nice to ask the boys and girls to choose. So they asked them. And the boys and girls thought for a long time—then they said that the beautiful windows with the light shining through should have the story of the Bible—what it had to say about God the Father, and His sending Jesus into the world.

And the big people agreed.

But there was still something else. The boys and girls said that the beautiful windows with the light shining through should have some words at the base, so that people could read them when they came into church.

And a second time the big people agreed.

And they asked the boys and girls what words should go there for the people to read. The boys and girls said that the words should be words out of the Bible itself—great words, and very short—'God is Love'.

But even that wasn't all. For the boys and girls remembered that many came into the church who could not read English—so they asked if the message could be in other languages, too.

A third time, the big people agreed. And it was so.

And now the words at the base of the story-windows that the light shines through in the beautiful church are in English, and in Latin, in Chinese, and in German, in Russian, and in Arabic. So now, people coming to worship from many lands—from the east and the west, and from the south and the north—can read the most wonderful message in the whole world: GOD IS LOVE (1 John 4[8]).

The Queen's Secret

ONCE UPON a time, I used to go to see a very old lady. And I always liked to go because she had a little basket full of beautiful coloured wools, and a little folder of needles. They were of all sizes, and sometimes when she had chosen one, she would ask me to thread it for her. I liked doing that—and she liked me to do it—because, like most boys and girls, I had sharp eyes and steady hands.

Then one day she suggested that I might like to thread a needle for myself, and do a little piece of embroidery. That was a proud day. I was delighted with the task of picking out the coloured wools, and matching them together.

When I had chosen my pattern and threaded my needle, my old friend showed me how to use it. And then she said a very wise thing—for she was a very wise old lady: 'My dear, I only prepared you a very small piece, for fear you might not be able to continue to the end. For it is a waste,' said she, 'to begin a beautiful thing like this, and not continue to the end.'

I never forgot that. And I was the more impressed when a little while ago I saw one of the most beautiful pieces of embroidery work in the world. It was done by Queen Mary, and is one of the largest ever done by a queen. It took her all the time she had to spare between 1941 and 1946—five long years. And sometimes she worked at it for seven or eight hours a day. Fancy working away at one piece of embroidery for five years! But Queen Mary had courage as well as skill, and she loved the beautiful colours.

The design was specially prepared from a bird and flower pattern of the eighteenth century, made to be worked by the Queen's needle in twelve large panels. When they were all worked—each part of the pattern, each beautiful colour in its proper place—Queen Mary meant to have them sewn together to make a carpet.

Each day she worked away at her beautiful colours, her needle going in and out. At first there were some things to puzzle over. Sometimes, when the work did not please her—as her lady-in-waiting noticed—the Queen would unpick it, and begin all over again. She never seemed to mind. She wanted her embroidery work, which would one day be a carpet, to be as beautiful as she could make it.

At last the happy day came when the last needle was threaded, and the last stitch put in. All twelve beautiful panels were finished—every one of a million stitches in its place. Five years had gone by, but now it was finished. Queen Mary had continued to the end, and what a happy end that was!

Then the twelve panels were carefully stitched together, and pressed out to make the carpet.

But what was to be done with it? That was the next

question. But Queen Mary—her needle going in and out—had been turning over that question for a long time, and already she had the answer. Britain had just finished a hard war, and she was poor. She needed dollars to help her people—and she could only get dollars by selling things to countries that had them. So Queen Mary decided to sell her beautiful carpet—not for herself—but for Britain.

And it was so. In the end, Queen Mary's beautiful carpet was sold to Canada for a hundred thousand dollars.

When the news got out, of course, everybody wanted to see it—first in Britain before it was packed up, and then in Canada.

One of those who came to see it in Canada was Johnny Kearse, from Ontario. Johnny and his teacher and school-mates stood before the beautiful carpet for a long time, and looked at it with wide-open eyes. And when Johnny saw how beautiful it was, and how big, and learned that its million stitches had all been done by an old lady, Queen Mary, he said something that those near him would never forget: 'It just shows,' said he, 'what you can do if you keep a-goin'!'

When Johnny's teacher heard that, she was so impressed with Johnny's words that she wrote them down, and sent them to England—to London, to Marlborough House, to Queen Mary herself. And when she read them she was very happy; and before long back came an answer—saying how happy the Queen was with what Johnny had said about her carpet: 'It just shows what you can do if you keep a-goin'!'

And that's a great secret—that was known by a queen.

Smokey Joe

MOTHER PUSSY looked a little anxious when people came to look at her new pussies. They were very new. So she looked right and left, and mewed a big motherly 'meow'. Then she gathered them in close.

They were happy, hungry little pussies, and her days became busier and busier as she taught them all the things that she wanted them to know.

First in the morning came their bath, when she licked them all over with very great care to make them presentable to the world. Then there were games—the kind of games that all little pussies play. And when they were tired, she gathered them around her again, and sang to them her best little 'meowing song'. It had only one verse, and she sang it over and over again—and it sounded to the little pussies very strong, and content and safe.

Before long the little pussies had learned to lap milk out of a saucer, and the kind man at the house where they lived put down a saucer for them very often. And they grew and grew, until one day Mother Pussy began to talk to them about what they would do in the big world. She told them of her own adventures when she was a young pussy. But always there were new adventures waiting—new things to do, new places to go to. 'No one,' said Mother Pussy, 'could tell what wonderful things might befall a young cat, if only he kept his wits about him.'

When she said that, one little pussy, who was now

two months old, was all eyes and ears. To go out into the world and have adventures was the very thing that he wanted. He did not realize then that there was work to be done in the world as well.

But soon he made that discovery—that the very happiest in the whole world are those who've something to do, something that they like doing, something that is of use to somebody.

And today there is no happier pussy in the world than Smokey Joe. He is three months old, and he earns sixpence a day as official rat-catcher at the Auckland National Airways Corporation. And there's nothing temporary about Smokey Joe's job—he is a real member of the staff. Before he came, the Corporation was troubled with rats in the basement. They ran about and made the place dirty, and sometimes ate up important papers. But that doesn't happen any more—not since Smokey Joe came.

And that was a proud morning that Smokey Joe would never forget. He was a Government servant—and all Government servants have to fill in a form and give a promise that they will give good service. So Smokey Joe filled in his form—a long, important-looking paper that would be kept in the office. It read, when it was finished:

1. Name of Applicant:
   (Surname) *Joe*
   (Christian names in full) *Smokey*
2. Nature of employment: *Rat-catcher*
3. Date, year and place of birth: *Approx.* 2 *Jan* 1952. *Kerosene case, Auckland.*
4. Whether married or single: *Single*
5. Details of post-primary education: *Uneducated as yet.*

And there were a lot more questions. But Smokey Joe filled them all in satisfactorily. Mr Arkle, the officer, talked to him for a little while and looked over his paper. Then he took out his pen and wrote on it: 'I have interviewed this applicant for the position of rat-catcher. While a little on the young side, I feel sure that with a little training he will be a worthy employee.'

And so it was settled. And Smokey Joe was the happiest little cat in the world—he had a real job to do and lots to learn about it so that he could do it better and better. And the people in the Airways office wondered how they had managed before Smokey Joe came—the youngest civil servant in Auckland.

The King's Sculptor

TRIT-TROT went the little donkey. Francis Chantery drove him into town. Two great milk barrels were over his brown, stubbly back, one on each side. Everybody in the little village of Norton knew Jock, and many in the big town of Sheffield. Francis kept a close eye on him as they trit-trotted along. Sometimes he could tell by the way he flicked his sharp, hairy ears what he was thinking about. But there were always times when the little donkey took Francis completely by surprise.

There was the morning when they came trit-trotting homewards with two empty barrels and the week's groceries. It was a hot morning. Francis drew rein as they came to a green pool beside the road. He was sure Jock would like a cool drink. But Jock quickly saw the chance of a joke as well as a drink.

In a trice he lay down in the pool, and would have rolled in the cool refreshing water, groceries and all, had his young driver not been quick. As it was, Francis had to rake the tea and the oatmeal and the sugar out of the pool, all dripping wet.

Francis liked better to remember, as they went along, the morning when they first met the little pussy. She had become a close friend, and in a few moments they would meet her again. Always since that first morning she waited for them, standing on her white, velvety toes on the sunny stone wall. And this morning, as they came trit-trotting along, she was there again. In one of the stones of the wall was a hollow just like a saucer, and Francis filled it with fresh, sweet milk.

Francis' father and mother were very poor, but Francis was happy enough. He liked especially his two friends, Jock and the little pussy on the wall. And sometimes he stopped in the market to peek through the rails where the farmer's pink, grunting pigs pushed each other about on the yellow straw. He loved all living things. And at night, when the lamp was lit, he lay on the rough mat on the hearth and drew little pictures of them. He drew Jock with his strong back, his long ears, and mischievous eyes. He loved Jock. And he drew a little gentle picture of the pussy on the wall. It was harder to draw the farmer's pigs. But he liked them. All things that had life—all things that God had made—seemed beautiful to him, even pigs.

One day when a gentleman was expected to dinner to do business with his father, Francis' mother made a large pie. And while she was busy tending her oven, Francis took some of the moist pastry for the top, and moulded it quickly. And his mother put it on the top of the pie.

At dinner-time, when the golden-crusted pie was brought on to the table, the important gentleman started back in surprise. 'But my dear Mrs Chantery,' said he, 'you should not have gone to all this expense for me. Such a pie, with all these pigs modelled on the top, must have cost you a lot. I can't remember that I have ever seen such a beautiful pie.'

Francis blushed to hear the great man's praise, and would have kept the secret had not his mother felt it only courteous to answer the gentleman. 'Be assured,' said she, 'that we did not spend money on the pie. I made it myself, and my small son here modelled the farmer's pigs on the top. We are poor people, and could never buy such a pie. Francis loves to draw and model. He finds beauty in odd places where most of us, I am afraid, do not think to look for it.'

And the honoured gentleman was very impressed. 'Some day,' said he, 'you will be a very famous man, my boy, and make a lot of money and be rich.'

But Francis did not want to be famous, or to be rich. The thing he wanted most in all the world was to love the simple and beautiful things that God had made, and show them to other people.

When he was only twelve, his father died, and he had to begin to work very hard to help his mother. But still he kept to his purpose. A man in Sheffield who owned a little shop offered him work, and every day he went to work for Mr Ramsey. He liked the little shop, and he liked Mr Ramsey, because he shared his love of beautiful things. In his little shop were pictures, and plaster models, and wood carvings.

He was eager to show Francis all that he knew, and to praise his efforts. 'Some day,' he said, 'you will be a very famous sculptor, my boy, and make a lot of money and be rich.'

But Francis cared not at all about being famous, or being rich. What he still wanted most in the world was to love the beautiful things, and to open the eyes of other people to see them. And when he had learned all that Mr Ramsey could teach him, he tied up his few chisels and modelling tools in a little bag and set off for London.

He was still very poor, and it cost a great deal to live in the city. And he missed his mother very much, and his animal friends too. But he earned enough to set up in an attic room, with one candle to light it at night. It was all rather simple, but Francis did not mind. He felt himself rich in the dream of all the beautiful things in the world.

By and by, people began to take notice of the things that he modelled. And the great artist, Benjamin West, allowed him to come into his studio while he worked on his painting of 'Christ Healing the Sick'. Francis loved the picture as it gradually took shape, but he wanted to model the head of the artist himself as he worked. The look in his eyes, the tenderness in his face as he looked at Jesus healing the sick, seemed very beautiful to Francis. 'People must see this beauty that God has put into the world on the face of the great artist,' he said. 'I must model it, so that it can be caught in stone for ever.' And he did. And everybody saw its beauty.

When it was decided to erect a figure of King George the Fourth, Francis was given the honour of making it. And it still stands in Trafalgar Square, right in the heart of London.

So by degrees Francis became the most famous sculptor in London, and by degrees the richest sculptor in London. But these things did not matter to him half so much as the happiness of being able to see and share beautiful things.

Old Shep

THE LITTLE town of Port Benton would never be the same again. The stationmaster said so; the men who kept the stores said so; the shepherd-men said so; the boys and girls who got out early from the little school said so.

Old Shep was dead.

Exactly at two o'clock that day, the Boy Scouts carried the casket to the bluff nearby. And the Rev. Ralph Underwood stood among the silent people.

Who was Old Shep?

Nobody there that day needed to ask who Old Shep was, as the Rev. Ralph Underwood chose his text from an old speech that a wise man had made years and years before: 'The one absolute, unselfish friend, that a man can have in this selfish world, the one that never deserts him, the one that never proves ungrateful or treacherous—is his dog.'

Yes, Old Shep was a dog—but no ordinary dog.

For years and years he had been about the station, meeting every train that came in. All he knew was that his master had gone away by train.

And the people of Fort Benton had become fond of Old Shep, and people travelling through by train had got into the habit of looking out when they came to Fort Benton. 'This is the place where the old dog comes out to meet the train,' they said. 'Let us see if we can see him.'

Always Old Shep, lonely, shaggy-coated, and faithful,

was there. Every time a train pulled in with a burst of steam, he was there.

He was plainly not a town dog. At first, he had not liked the sounds and smells of a station, but he had got used to them. One day, when a flock of sheep came by, Old Shep lifted up his heels and ran after them with a joyous bark. It was plain to those who watched that day that he loved sheep and understood them. But for six long years nobody knew any more.

And then they knew it all. Old Shep's master had been a shepherd-man, a lonely man, and a sick one, living away up in the hills. His name was Tony.

Going once to his hut, somebody remembered him nursing two little sick lambs, and an old ewe with a sore nose. He didn't have much to say. But there was no doubt that he understood his animal friends. And there was no doubt of the bond between Tony and Old Shep. His great brown kindly eyes followed him everywhere.

At last the day came when Tony—too sick to stay alone any more—went away on the train from Fort Benton. He did not know that it was for the last time. Old Shep watched him go, but he was not greatly troubled—always he had come back.

At once Old Shep found himself a comfortable place underneath the baggage-room platform—and waited.

But days went by and nights went by. When winter came, and snow lay on the ground, the kind station-master tried to coax Old Shep inside the station. But he was happy where he was. He wanted to stay where he could watch the trains come in. He could not know that his master would never come back.

And so he kept his faithful watch—for days and weeks and years.

Then one sad day, the news went out—out to his friends at the station, out to those who travelled through, and then out to the whole world, copied by the great newspapers, and flashed by the wireless.

That was why, on that January day in 1942, the stationmaster lowered the flag to half-mast, and the shopkeepers shut their shops, and the boys and girls left their school desks, and the Scouts carried a casket up on to a little hill. That was why the Rev. Ralph Underwood stood in their midst to speak an unforgettable word about faithfulness.

And today a simple monument marks Old Shep's grave—floodlit at night, when the trains pass through—so that travellers from afar can hear a story of great faithfulness. And always the men and women and boys and girls to whom it is told lift up their hearts and try a little better themselves.

Seedtime and Harvest

DAVID FIFE, the farmer's boy, was going home.

'You'll forget,' cried his old friend the farmer as he waved him goodbye. David had loved the wide grain fields of Canada, lying under the great sky. But now he was homesick. He wanted to go home.

He shifted his bundle from one shoulder to the other. It was light that morning. As he set off to seek a ship, the last words wafted to him were those of his old friend the farmer: 'You'll forget . . . !'

But David didn't forget.

He had been no time back in Glasgow when he set out to buy the Scotch bonnet he had promised. He wanted it to be a fine Scotch bonnet, since it was a promise. And in a little shop just off the city cobblestones he found what he sought.

The shopkeeper wrapped it rather solemnly and took his money. But David wasn't solemn. His heart was light—he was home, he had remembered his promise, and the day was fine.

He turned his steps eagerly toward the docks. He would see what was going on down there. His heart took a leap as he came within sight of the tangle of tall masts. Where had all these fine ships come from? Where were they going? What were they carrying?

One of the tallest, David discovered, had come from Danzig, and was carrying grain. Some of the grain, golden and hard, lay spilled on the dock-side. If it stayed there, it was more than certain the little dock mice would find it and carry it away. But before Mr and Mrs Mouse could discover it, David stooped down, and picked it up.

'What beautiful grain,' said he, as he let it flow through his fingers. 'It would be a pity to let the mice have this.'

Then he thought of his old farmer friend in Canada. Perhaps he would like to see it. It would be a surprise for him. And he tucked a few grains of the new wheat into the Scotch bonnet he had bought.

For months and months after David had sent off his parcel, he heard nothing of it. He even wondered whether it had lost its way.

But no. Before the spring, his old farmer friend untied his parcel.

'What is this?' he asked as he fumbled with the string. Then he remembered his parting words to young David: 'You'll forget. . . .' But it was now plain he hadn't forgotten.

The old farmer put on his Scotch bonnet.

'But what joke is this the young rascal has got up

to?' he asked, as a trickle of wheat ran down his fingers and on to the floor. 'What joke is this?'

Then he stooped, as David had done, and picked it up.

'But it's beautiful grain,' said he. 'Full and golden it is. I wonder if it would grow out here?'

Carefully he handled it, and when the time came he prepared a little corner of his field.

The days went by, and the nights went by. The spring rains fell, and the sun came, and tiny green shoots pushed their way up. The old farmer watched eagerly, and they grew, till near harvest they were full of promise.

Then suddenly a sad thing happened. Cattle broke in one night, and in their haste, trampled down all the new heads of grain—all but three. The old farmer took a stout stick to the cattle and chased them out. But it was no use. All that he could do was to comfort his sad heart as he looked at the trampled heads of his precious crop. 'There are three left. I will take care of these.'

When they were fully ripened, he put them away safely in a little dry place. And when next seedtime came, he lifted them out carefully and sowed them where he knew they would be safe.

At harvest-time, he was able to gather a fine, fat bag of golden grain.

Next year he sowed them again, and again harvested them, multiplied by the miracle of sun, shower, and loving care.

And soon the fame of his good harvests got abroad, and farmers came seeking the precious Red Fife wheat —*named after the farmer's boy who had remembered his promise.*

And always God remembered His greater promise —that seedtime and harvest should not fail. And the great grain elevators of Ontario were filled with the hard, sweet, beautiful Red Fife—all sprung from the three heads!

And year by year now in Canada, as in our country, the grain is gathered into the church at Harvest Festival time with rejoicings and hymns, to thank God for His goodness. And no wonder! Always God keeps His promise! Seedtime and harvest do not fail!

We plough the fields, and scatter
The good seed on the land,
But it is fed and watered
By God's Almighty hand;
He sends the snow in winter,
The warmth to swell the grain,
The breezes, and the sunshine,
And soft refreshing rain.

He only is the Maker
Of all things near and far;
He paints the wayside flower,
He lights the evening star;
The winds and waves obey Him,
By Him the birds are fed;
Much more to us, His children,
He gives our daily bread.

Anna's Secret

IN THE green, green land of Ireland stood a little white house. It was only a very little house, with a chimney-corner. Everybody in the town of Antrim knew the little white house—the house of Anna and Jamie.

Jamie was the shoemaker, and the little white house served for workshop as well. In one corner stood a bench. And beside it a wooden tub where Jamie soaked the leather to soften it for the feet of Antrim. Far into the night sometimes could be heard the tap-tap of his hammer. But there were poor times, too, when no one came to the door with a hole in his shoe, and silver in his pocket.

Someone up in the great city invented a machine that would do in minutes what it took Jamie all day to do. And few wanted shoes made in the slow, good, patient way. And few wanted shoes mended in the little white house, with the tap-tap of Jamie's hammer. And it was hard to buy bread, and Jamie and Anna, and the little children whom God had given them, went hungry to bed.

Inside the door of the little white house that opened with a welcome to all who knocked was a plain, clean table, and a dresser and crocks. Anna loved her dresser and crocks, and she loved her cup and saucer with its pattern of blue, that stands there to this day. Often and often she pushed it along the table when no one was looking, so that a little child could have the last sweet sup and the sugar at the bottom.

The little white house had no chairs, but what matter of that? It had stools—one for each, and a spare one for a weary old beggar, or a friend. For all Antrim knew their way to the little white house. They came with their joys—over the cobbles—and they came with their sorrows. They came when their pockets were full, and when they were empty. And always there was a warm welcome, and Anna stirred the peat fire in the chimney-corner.

As constant as the seasons, Anna sat in her chimney-corner.

On Sundays she whitewashed the hearth-stone, and

draped her little shawl over her shoulders. And however hungry and hard the week had been, Sunday was a glad day. She hung the kindly kettle on its hook over the fire, and to those whose hearts were tuned to hear, it sang a song of peace.

On Sundays when Anna put on her little cap and shawl, the children thought that she had the most beautiful face in Antrim. And, indeed, they were right. But always the grown-up people of Antrim knew—whatever the day—that Anna had the most beautiful hands in Antrim. They were not soft hands—as were some in the great houses—nor unlined. Anna's hands could never be that—not whilst she lived in the little white house in Antrim. But they were beautiful hands—the most beautiful hands in Antrim. And one day she told the secret to old Liza Lecky as they sat together. The secret, said Anna that day in the chimney-corner, as she tried to ease old Liza's sad heart, was in having hands that served. And anyone who loved God, and knew the secret, could have beautiful hands, for said she, 'God takes a han' wherever He can find it, and jist diz what He likes wi' it. Sometimes He takes a bishop's, and lays it on a child's head in benediction, then He takes th' han' of a a docther t' relieve pain, th' han' of a mother t' guide her child, an' sometimes He takes th' han' of an aul craither like me t' give a bit o' comfort to a neighbour. But they're all han's touch't be His Spirit, an' His Spirit is everywhere lukin' fur han's to use.'

Oranges and Bananas

THE LITTLE Italian fruit-seller was busy with his trays. Day after day he hawked his trays of fruit—oranges and bananas—to the offices and shops of Boston. They were worth only a few dimes, but he was happy.

On Saturday night he set out in rows his little piles of dimes. Sometimes he had bigger coins, too. It took a long time for the piles to grow. Always there was the fruit to buy before he could sell it, and his room to pay for, and his food. And sometimes he needed a pair of shoes. Sometimes a shirt.

But one Saturday night as he set them out, he found that there were a few coins over—and next week there were a few more. Little Johnny was growing rich.

Near where he plied his simple trade there rose into the sky a great building with 'Boston Public Library' written over it. Johnny saw people going in and coming out. Some went in with books, some came out with books. Some carried no books—nothing that Johnny could see, unless it was that they carried something within their hearts and minds, gathered in the great library. Johnny was curious.

And one day when he had not to go so far with his trays of fruit, he stepped into the great library to satisfy his curiosity. The great library was full of books. Never before had Johnny seen so many books—books full of the wisdom of the ages. Shyly he took down one from the shelves. 'I wonder if there is any book here,' said he to himself, 'to tell a humble fruit-seller what to do with his money—the little piles of coins that are over at the end of the week?'

After much searching, Johnny found such a book. It told him what to do with his money—how to invest it wisely and steadily. And the little fruit-seller went back to his work.

Gradually Saturday by Saturday the little piles grew, until at the end of years Johnny owned large blocks of shops and offices, and land for building.

And by the time he was old, he knew that he was really rich. 'But all these things are not for myself,' said he. 'No one should keep the good things for himself.' Johnny could never forget that above everything he owed a debt to the Boston Public Library.

At last his mind was made up. With a bulging pocket, he set off for the Public Library. He walked straight in with a light step, and knocked on the office door of the Chief Librarian. When Mr Milton Lord opened the door to him and heard his story, he was surprised. But his eyes opened wider still when Johnny laid on his desk one and a half million dollars. 'But what are these for?' he asked. Said Johnny: 'They are to pay my debt—my debt of thanksgiving for all the good things that your library has taught me. You can buy some more books with these, and some day I will come again with a bulging pocket, and pay off a little more of the debt I owe.'

When Johnny had gone, Mr Milton Lord rushed off to tell the good news to his fellow members of the Library Board. And when they saw the dollars and heard the promise of more, they were as surprised and happy as he. 'But,' said they, 'who is this generous man, who is giving the Library one and a half million dollars?'

'His name,' said the Librarian, 'is Johnny Deferrari.'

Then he told them the story of the little fruit-seller, and the wisdom that he had found in the great library. But most of all he told them of the wonderful thankfulness that he had found in his heart. And those men knew that Johnny had a great secret, for '*It is more blessed to give than to receive*' (Acts 20[35]).

The Wise Son

ONCE UPON a time there lived in India a good man who had two sons. They all lived together and were very happy.

But by and by the father became old and grey, and knew that the time must soon come for him to die. 'Before I die,' said he, 'I want to find the wisest thing to do with my house and my wealth. I have worked hard all my life, buying and selling sweet-smelling spices, and the things that the people have needed. And now I have become a rich merchant. I have my two good sons, and I shall leave the care and honour of my wealth to the wiser of them. But it is not an easy task to decide which one is to have it.'

And the old merchant sat and thought and thought. 'I will set them a test,' said he. And late that evening, when the cool hour had come, he called them into his presence. 'My sons,' said he, 'tomorrow morning I want you to go into the market and each buy for me something that will fill the whole of my house.' Then into the hands of each son he placed a coin—an anna. 'It is a test,' said he, 'I want to find out which is the wiser, fit to carry the honour and care of my wealth when I am gone. Do you agree?'

And the two sons agreed, and took the coins, and bade their old father good night.

And early in the morning, before the sun shone in the market-place, they rose and washed and dressed and made their way thither. As they moved about, more and more people came to the market-place, and there were more and more things to see. Soon they separated, and each went his way.

The first son moved quickly from stall to stall. On one there was rice—but he could not buy much for the coin in his hand. The next offered beautiful fruits, juicy and kissed by the sun—but he could not buy many for his coin. Then he saw a stall piled high with cotton, yards and yards—but that was no use.

From stall to stall he passed quickly. And the morning wore on. 'There must be something somewhere,' he told himself, 'that I can buy cheaply for my coin, something that will fill my father's house. On and on he went. Just before nightfall he came to a stall, where men were selling golden straw. 'Straw is light,' said he with relief, 'and cheap,' said he. 'Surely it is the cheapest thing in the market. I will buy straw.' And he struck the best bargain he could, and the man took his little coin.

But when at sundown he brought home his load of straw, it did not nearly fill the house—to his grief it hardly covered the floor. And he wondered how his brother had fared. All day long he had been too busy to think of him—too busy thinking about himself.

But at last, as the kindly night fell, his brother came from the market-place. He had spent a long day in his search, but now as night fell it was at an end, and he came bringing what would fill the whole house.

When the old father saw what his son carried, he was deeply pleased. 'You are the wise one,' he said. 'You have shown true wisdom,' said he. 'You are worthy to take charge of my wealth and all that is mine.' For the second son had bought—well, can you guess?—yes, he had bought tiny candles. And that night as they were lighted and set about, they filled the whole of his father's house.

Long, long ago, One who was even wiser than the merchant's wise son spoke of the pure light of a little candle. He said that boys and girls and everybody who loved Him, and did His will in the world, were like little shining candles set in dark places. 'Let your light so shine before men,' He said, 'that they may see your good works, and glorify your Father which is in Heaven.' And boys and girls to this day remember His words when they sing:

Jesus bids us shine with a clear, pure light,
Like a little candle burning in the night.

The Little Conceited Girl

THERE WAS once a little conceited girl called Elizabeth. And she had six sisters. One day Elizabeth and all her sisters went to church—only they didn't call it church, they called it Meeting, because their father and mother were Quakers, and that is what they called their Church.

Elizabeth and her sisters sat all in a row, and Elizabeth wore purple shoes with scarlet laces, but because she thought she looked very smart in her little purple shoes and scarlet laces she was restless. Her eyes wandered down towards her feet, and she did not think very much about what was being said in Meeting.

But when the preacher began his sermon, little conceited Elizabeth suddenly forgot all about her shoes. The words of the preacher made her think of many, who were just as dear to God as she was, who couldn't have any shoes or laces at all. And she felt that she wanted to help.

At once she gave up wearing purple shoes with scarlet laces, and began to think only of how she could help. In the town where she lived there were lots of little boys and girls who had no chance of going to school, because they were poor. So Elizabeth, when she grew up, opened a school for them. And the children loved Elizabeth and they loved her school.

Then she married a good man called Joseph Fry, and went to live in London. But always she was thinking about the poor people, and the unhappy people. In London there were lots of these. She went to visit them. Sometimes their houses were horrid and dark, small and dirty. Sometimes their windows wouldn't open to let in the air. Sometimes their doors wouldn't close properly, and they had no beds, and had to sleep on the floors. And very often they had sick babies because they lived in such horrid houses.

Elizabeth Fry took them food and clothes and books and medicines. Sometimes when she had tidied them up she would say, 'I will read you a story.' And she would stop and read them one of the stories of Jesus who had changed her conceited little heart into a kind heart.

Then one day she heard about the poor people who were in prison. Many of them hadn't done very bad things at all! And the prison was a horrible place, all dark and damp and full of beetles and rats, and overcrowded with people. When a poor father and mother were put in prison they had to take their children too, because there was nowhere else for them to go. They hadn't real beds to sleep on, and they hadn't real tables on which to have their meals, and it was all very horrid.

Elizabeth Fry began visiting a big prison where there were over three hundred people all crowded together. And they were very dirty because they couldn't wash.

Soon she had them washing their hands and faces and tidying up their hair. And soon they tidied up their prison, and Elizabeth started a school in the prison for the little children. She said: 'They will not always be in prison. We must help them to grow up good and true. They are just as dear to God as anybody.'

She found needles and scissors and stuff and got the mothers sewing, and in less than a year they made twenty thousand garments to wear. Wasn't that lovely? And because they were happier and cleaner and busier, they were better behaved and many of them got let out of prison.

Then Elizabeth went to other prisons, and started all over again. She got people to help her, and she went all over the land—and by and by to other lands. Everywhere she went, people listened to her: great people who made the laws, and kings and queens. But nothing could make her conceited any more. People said she was the most famous woman in the world, but in her heart there was only love—love for God, and love for the people—so, of course, she couldn't be conceited any more.

Old Achor's Secret

NOBODY IN the city was better known than old Achor. He sat with his little collecting bowl outside the market. Early in the morning, when the people brought down their fruits and nuts and hens to sell, he was there, holding out his little bowl. People said that his name meant 'trouble', and, indeed, he seemed always to be in trouble, for always his cry was the same: 'A gift in the name of God! Remember the poor! Remember the poor!'

In the early morning, as the people made their way to the market, most were in too big a hurry to notice old Achor. But he did not cease to cry, or to hope that someone would come by and put a tiny coin in his bowl.

There were other beggars in the city—some blind, some crippled, one that hobbled on two sticks, another that had to be lifted on to his pitch by his friends. But there was nothing like that about old Achor. He was not blind, he was not crippled, he could walk to his chosen begging place outside the market. And little by little people came to believe that he was a beggar because he liked getting things for nothing, and was lazy at heart. But whether that was so or not, the old fellow was always at his pitch outside the market, always with his begging bowl, always crying the same: 'A gift in the name of God! Remember the poor! Remember the poor!'

And always there were people coming and going:

going to the market early in the morning with their fruits and nuts and hens, coming away later with money in their pockets. He heard their market chatter, and knew always when prices had been good.

But one morning as he listened to their market chatter he heard a more amazing thing than the rising prices of fruits and nuts and hens. When first it reached his ears he could hardly believe it. But soon another little knot of people came by talking about it, and Achor took special notice. And soon all the people returning from the market were talking about it, and he knew it must be true.

The King, they said, was soon to pass that way in all his splendour. The little children were excited, because many of them had never seen the King. And old Achor was most excited of all, though he tried to keep it to himself. He rubbed his collecting bowl smooth and shiny as he thought about it. 'Surely the King will take notice of this shiny bowl,' said he, 'and will give me something as befits a king. It might be a piece of gold.' And Achor's eyes lit up at the thought of it. 'A king could never give anything less than a piece of gold.' And old Achor thought and thought about his coming good fortune. And as he thought on it, always it became more and more wonderful. 'Perhaps,' said he to himself, 'he will give me a jewel, and make me rich for ever.' But old Achor was still troubled—troubled this time that he did not know exactly what the King would give him, and at what hour he would come. He was troubled also lest the crowd would be so great that the King would not hear his cry: 'A gift in the name of God! Remember the poor! Remember the poor!'

And the hours passed by, and the sun beat down hot upon the market, and old Achor had no thought for the rising prices—his thought was only of what he was going to get for nothing.

Then the great hour came. The King in royal procession passed along the way. And old Achor's heart thumped with excitement. Next minute, the King was standing right in front of him. And then a most amazing thing happened. At first old Achor thought he must be dreaming. But no, it was quite true, and he hadn't lost his wits. There was the King standing right in front of him—and before ever he could get out his cry, the King himself was saying it: 'A gift in the name of God! A gift in the name of God!' And the old beggar suddenly realized that the King hadn't come that way to give—but to receive. And he put his trembling hand into his little bowl, and closed his fingers on the few coins that were there, and gave them to the King.

And the great procession passed on.

But in that moment of giving—instead of getting—a new happiness of such a wonderful kind came flooding into the heart of old Achor that he found that he wanted to be on the move, too. And he flung off his beggar's cloak, and dropped his little begging bowl, and went after the King. And people forgot that old Achor's name meant 'trouble'—because he was so changed—and they called him Arnon instead, which means 'leaping for joy'.

What a pity it was that it took the old fellow so long to find the secret—Jesus knew it always. He said: 'It is more blessed to give than to receive.' And because that is still one of the most important secrets in the world, it is written down in our Bibles (Acts 20[35]).

God's Birds

JACK MINER's heart was one of the kindest in the world. Everybody at Kingsville knew it. Even the birds knew it.

Every season they came flying across Canada, across the lakes and mountains and forests—great birds, wild ducks and wild geese, flying on strong, swift wings. They felt safe in the sanctuary Jack had made for them.

Year by year more and more came. And Jack became more and more curious to know how far they had come, and which way. If only he could understand their talk—'quack-quack' and 'cackle-cackle'—but that was impossible. So he had to think out another way.

All too soon, when the snows came and covered all the food, they would fly off. Where would they fly, and which way?

Before they left, Jack caught a few of them, and fixed on to their legs tiny bands. On the tiny bands Jack printed clearly and carefully his name and address. Then he could do no more but trust to the kind interest of unknown men, who might come across his friends in that far unknown land, to write and tell him where they had got to.

And one day a letter did come—after he had waited a long time. Jack was excited. And what the letter said gave Jack another shining idea. At last he knew that some of his birds flew to where men and women lived who had never heard of God. Jack could not bear to think that anyone should not know of the Great, Loving Father. 'Wouldn't it be a grand idea,' he said to himself, 'to send them some messages from the Bible. Then they would know.' And he set about his plan.

On one side of the tiny leg bands, where there was room, he printed clearly and finely, short messages such as 'God is Love'.

The birds came again, flying on swift, strong wings. And went again. And another long time went by.

At last a telegram came. Eagerly Jack opened it. What would it have to say? He read: 'Am on my way to your home with several leg bands, placed on birds by you, and taken off by Indians and Eskimos in the Arctic Circle.'

What story would the sender have to tell of his birds? And of those far-away Indian and Eskimo people? Jack could hardly wait.

And when the Rev. Mr Walton came it was a story far more wonderful than anything Jack had imagined. The birds, flying with their tiny leg bands, had carried the messages to the people. And those far-away Indian and Eskimo people knew that God loved them. 'They believe these messages are sent direct from God,' said Mr Walton.

Every Sunday the little Mission hut filled up to hear the simple messages explained. 'They think,' said Mr Walton, a second time, 'that these messages come to them direct from God—as indeed, they do.' And then he added something that made Jack very, very happy. 'Many of these far-away people,' said he, 'who have now learned for the first time that the Great Father loves them, have become good Indian and Eskimo Christians.'

'Those Indians and Eskimos are not mistaken,' said Jack, 'for God does send messages to us in all sorts of ordinary ways. Jesus said so. To the people who listened to Him, He said, "Look at the birds of the air! Look at the common flowers of the grass! Sown by the winds, watered by the rains, tinted by the sun! See how beautiful they are! *If God, the Loving Father fares for birds and flowers—surely He will much more care cor you!*" '

And Jack, the good bird-man, and his new friend rejoiced together over God's birds that had become missionaries to His far-away children.

Peter's Pocket-knife

It's great fun to get a parcel through the post. A letter is fun, but a parcel is better still.

That's what Peter thought. Peter's parcel was a small, knobbly one addressed in Grandfather's best handwriting. He couldn't get the string undone quick enough; he couldn't get the paper off quick enough. What was inside? In a minute he knew. Inside was a bright-bladed pocket-knife. A real beauty! Just the thing he wanted. And Grandfather had put in a little card: 'Love from Grandfather to Peter.' And on the other side were five more words that Peter couldn't quite make out: 'All power is a trust.'

'What does that mean, Mummy?' asked Peter. Then, turning to his father, 'Daddy, what does it mean?' And both Father and Mother said, 'You must wait and ask Grandfather to tell you when he comes over.'

So when Grandfather came over for tea on Saturday, the first minute he was in his favourite chair by the window Peter asked, 'Please, Grandfather, what did the five words mean?'

Grandfather's eyes twinkled. 'Which five words?' asked he. ' "Love from Grandfather to Peter." ? '

'No,' said Peter. 'No, Grandfather. That's easy. I know what those words mean. No. The other five.'

'Ah!' said Grandfather. 'Let me see. Now, I think that's easy, too. Let me tell you a story.'

And Peter closed up his pocket-knife and scrambled up on to the window-seat by Grandfather's chair—for that was always the seat he liked for a story.

'Is it a true story?' asked Peter, his eyes on Grandfather's face.

'Yes. It's a true story,' said Grandfather. 'And it's about a boy called Peter.'

'Oh,' said Peter, 'it's a make-up story.'

'No; it isn't,' said Grandfather. 'It's a quite true story, as you will know when I've told it to you.

'This other Peter lived in London, with a lot of other boys. In the day-time he went to Westminster School, near the great Abbey—Westminster Abbey, where the kings and queens are crowned, and many good and great people are remembered, poets and princes and prime ministers. It is a very ancient church with beautiful windows, full of all the shining colours of the rainbow, reaching up to the lofty roof. And before the high altar and pulpit for the preacher, there is the place for the people to pray, or to stand for the hymns when the beautiful organ is played and the choir sings.

'And there are many beautiful chapels, and gates of oak and bronze, with stories worked into them of the great deeds of the past. And in King Henry the Seventh's Chapel—the most beautiful of all—are little seats down each side for the knights, with a red-and-gold sword on the front of each. Above, are hung beautiful banners, so beautiful in their designs and colours that you could look at them all day. And there are lots of other things to see in the Abbey, as Peter the schoolboy discovered. When lessons were over, he and his school-mates often spent some time in the Abbey. There were so many ancient and wonderful and beautiful things to see. And, of course, there was the Coronation Chair, in which all the English Sovereigns have been crowned for six hundred years. No wonder it is so precious! It is a quite plain wooden chair now that some of its brightness has gone, with two high arms to rest upon, and a fine, high-pointed back to lean against. Some of its beautiful decorations still remain. And underneath is a great stone, so old that nobody knows how old it is. It is over a thousand years old. No wonder it is so precious!

'Well, one night, after Peter and his friends had been in the Abbey, something happened. Somehow, Peter got locked in after all the other people had gone. Nobody quite knew how it happened—whether he boasted to his friends that he wouldn't be afraid to sleep in the Abbey all night, or whether he just missed the closing time, wandering around looking at all the beautiful things, and got left in by mistake.

'Anyway, Peter stayed in the Abbey all night by himself. Of course, there was nothing to hurt him—but there was no bed, and in the velvety darkness he wondered where he would sleep. At last, he decided that the precious Coronation Chair would be a good place. So he climbed up into it, and curled round like a puppy—and went to sleep.

'He slept soundly all night, but in the morning he wakened early, when the first light came through the tall beautiful windows, with their reds and blues and purples and golds. Peter sat up and stretched, and looked about him, and rubbed the sleep out of his eyes. But he knew it must still be very, very early. Then, for something to do, he turned out all the things in his pocket. And there was his pocket-knife.

'Then he did a dreadful thing—for a boy called Peter with a pocket-knife—he carved his name on the precious Coronation Chair. And he carved it so deeply that it could never be got off—and you can still read it there today: "Peter Abbott slept in this chair July 5, 1800." Now, wasn't that a dreadful thing to do?'

And as Grandfather's story ended, Peter, who sat curled up on the window-seat listening to him, agreed that it was. And suddenly he saw why Grandfather had put the second five words on the little card with his pocket-knife: 'All power is a trust.' A pocket-knife gave a boy new power to do all sorts of things he had never done before—but it was a power that *he had to be trusted to use in the right way*. And Peter's Grandfather said that all new powers were like that.

So Peter kept the little card that came through the post with his pocket-knife, with its five words on one side: 'Love from Grandfather to Peter', and on the other side another five words now just as easy to understand: 'All power is a trust.'

All Things Bright and Beautiful

THE WARM June sunshine flooded into the ancient, narrow streets, and even the tiniest child felt the joy of it. The lovely old English city of York, with its great Minster, and its narrow streets and mighty stone walls, was full of people. They had come from far and near for a gala to celebrate the Coronation of King George the Fifth. And they were wearing their gladdest and gayest clothes.

It was such a special occasion—the beginning of a new reign. But little could anyone guess that it was also the beginning of something else—something that would grow in beauty every year through the King's reign, and to the very ends of the earth.

In the sunny streets, among the jostling people in their gladdest and gayest clothes, was an old gardener whom nobody took any notice of. He had come especially to see the display of flowers which was part of the gala. Among them were plain blue and white flowers called lupins. They were a pleasant shape, sturdy and strong, reaching up like little spires into the sky—but their colours were only blue and white. Most people passed them by without sparing them a second look—but not old George Russell the gardener. He stood a long time looking at their pleasant shape, strong and sturdy, reaching up like little spires.

And then a wonderful thought came to old George Russell the gardener: 'Wouldn't it be wonderful,' said he, 'if flowers of this shape could be of different colours.' But nobody in that crowded city had any idea what the old gardener was thinking. Their thoughts were full of other things.

But old George Russell could not forget. And the next day he set about collecting lupins for his garden. He even sent to far parts of the world, where they had lupins that were a little different.

With loving care, he prepared the ground and planted the seed, and when the little plants came up and put out leaves, he watched them every day with loving care. And he got the bees to help him, and he crossed and re-crossed the flowers, saving each time only the best ones. All the others he cast away. It took a long, long time, and much skill and patience.

Every sunny June when the flowering season came, the old gardener waited with eagerness to see what colours would come on his lupins. And in time, here and there beautiful colours began to show—added to the spires sturdy and strong that reached up into the sky. At first, there was only one new colour, then three or four, then six or seven.

In time, news got out about the beautiful lupins. People told each other about them, but even the cleverest gardeners could not believe their ears. So they found their way to old George Russell's garden. And they were delighted with what they saw—and they wanted to buy the seed. One visitor from America offered a handful of dollars for 'just a thimbleful of seed'. But, no, the old gardener would not sell. Another offered fifty pounds of English money. But no, he would not sell. And more colours were added.

At last—after twenty-five years had gone by—old gardener George Russell knew one day that his task was done. At last, after all those years of skill and patience, there were sixty new colours, each one of them named—sixty beautiful colours as rich and lovely as the rainbow; pink and orange, yellow, strawberry-pink, royal purple and gold, rose-pink and a beautiful violet, and lots more.

Looking back, it seemed hard to believe that at the Coronation of King George the Fifth there had been only plain blue and white lupins. And now—just in time for the Coronation of King George the Sixth—as part of the gala celebration of his coming to the throne—there were sixty beautiful colours.

It had taken all the years between the crowning of one king and the next, but at last the old gardener, with great happiness, knew that his task was done. People came from all over the world to see the lupins. The Royal Horticultural Society gave the old gardener its gold medal; and then, as another honour, they called the beautiful new lupins, sturdy and strong, upreaching to the skies in sixty beautiful colours, Russell lupins. *But his greatest reward of all was in knowing that he had helped God add some more beauty to the world.*

God is always looking for people—grown-ups and boys and girls—to help Him add more beauty to the world. There are, of course, lots of ways of doing it—by kindly thoughts, by courageous actions, by happy laughter. There are ever so many ways.

The Emperor's Window

ONCE upon a time, in a country far away, a new emperor reigned. He was very young, and very strong, and very tall. And when he was dressed, he felt that he looked very handsome.

Always, first thing, when he opened his eyes in the morning, he thought, 'Today I must wear my fine clothes.'

And when he got up, the first thing he did was to dress and walk up and down in front of a mirror. He walked this way and that, he looked this way and that. To his old servant he gave orders to draw back the rich folds of the curtains, so that more light could come into his room. Up and down in front of the mirror he paced.

Not surprisingly, his kingdom grew poor. His merchants quarrelled with other merchants, and refused to pay honest wages for honest work. Those entrusted with the law let all sorts of cruel and evil things happen.

But no tidings of these things reached the young Emperor.

Every now and again, he had his old servant take down his mirror and replace it with a larger—the small mirror with the middle-size mirror, and the middle-size mirror with a great mirror.

Then one day suddenly all was changed.

It was the old servant who found the secret. One night when the young Emperor was asleep, he visited his room. There was no light in it, save what came from the moon where the curtains were drawn back. But he moved quickly and quietly to his task. Under the fold of his cloak he carried the carpenter's saw, and before he replaced the middle-sized mirror with the great mirror he swiftly and carefully ran a saw round the edge of it, in the way that the palace carpenter had shown him. Then with a little gentle push he pushed out the square in the wall, and as quickly and quietly, while the Emperor slept, covered it with the great mirror.

The young Emperor was very pleased with the great mirror. As he paced up and down, it served him better than any.

But the old servant was sick at heart. He saw that the time to do something had come. And a second time he crept into the Emperor's room while he slept. There was no light in it, save what came from the moon where the curtains were drawn back. But he moved quickly and quietly to his task. With one mighty effort, he took down the great mirror, and bore it away.

In the morning, when the young Emperor wakened as usual, to pace up and down admiring himself, he got the shock of his life. There was no mirror there. Instead, for the first time, he saw his people going by outside. He saw little children pale and thin for want of bread. He saw old grandfathers and grandmothers begging, because they had no money. He saw fathers and mothers with deeply anxious faces, because they knew not where to turn for help.

And it was all a great shock.

Without a word, the old servant stood by to see the

miracle happen. And it did happen. The young Emperor tore from his proud back his fine clothes, and called for simple ones that would enable him to serve. And he went out into the poor street with his people, and they gathered round him—even the merchants and the keepers of the law. And they all did what they could to make the kingdom happy and prosperous once more. And the old servant, smiling wisely, was content, for at last the young Emperor had learned to look not only on his own things, but also on the things of others (Philippians 2[4]).

The Little Blue-eyed Flower

WHAT DO you do when you first get into bed? Do you go to sleep straight away, or do you play a little game in the velvety darkness when the light goes out, and before you are ready to go to sleep? I used to do that often—especially in the winter-time. But then I had a sister—that was one of the advantages of having a twin-sister, that we shared games at bedtime.

In the summer, when the days were long and full of sunshine and picnics and work and play, we were often so sleepy at bedtime that we could have fallen into bed with all our clothes on, and never noticed it. There were no games then. But in the winter-time when the days were short and the nights long, we had lovely games—quiet games when we were tubbed, with our prayers said, and tucked snugly under the blankets.

One of the best was called 'The Flower Game'. We made it up ourselves. It began in order of the alphabet: A B C right down to Z—though we never got down to Z in one night. We were always asleep long before that. The game was to start with A and in turn to name all the flowers we could think of with A—and see who got the most. A for asters; A for arum lilies; A for antirrhinums; A for anemones—and so on. Then when we had exhausted A we went on to B, and then on to C and D and E until we ended up with the only name we knew for Z—Z for zinnias. But in between, we got to know lots of the lovely names of the flowers—until they weren't just like a crowd of unknown boys and girls without any names, but were like a lot of boys and girls who had become playmates and friends, with their names all known. For flowers have names—every one of them—and some of them very pretty, just like boys and girls.

There is a nice little legend which tells us that right at the beginning of the world, when God was giving the flowers their names, one little flower forgot her name—and at the end of the naming, she had to come back and ask what her name was. And somebody put that legend into a charming little verse:

When to the flowers so beautiful
The Father gave a name,
Back came a little blue-eyed one
(All timidly it came),
And standing at its Father's feet,
And gazing in His face,
It said in low and trembling tones
With sweet and gentle grace,
'Dear God, the name Thou gavest me,
Alas, I have forgot.'
Then kindly looked the Father down,
And said, 'Forget-me-not.'

Do you know that little flower today? It grows in many simple gardens where there is moisture and sun enough, or by streams in country places. It has still a little blue face, and it's still called forget-me-not.

Wouldn't it be dreadful to forget your own name? A name means so much. It is something very personal and special—not only for writing on your books at school, but for play with your friends, and for lots of other things just as special and important. It would be very awkward when Mother called you to come in to dinner if you'd forgotten your name. It would be very awkward when the postie came with a letter addressed to you if you'd forgotten your name.

Fortunately, that is not very likely to happen—not now. It might happen to very tiny boys and girls—very tiny ones before they can properly talk—but it is not very likely to happen to you. You are not like the little blue-eyed flower that forgot its name, the forget-me-not.

But I wonder if you are ever likely to forget God?

One thing you can be quite sure of is that He doesn't forget you—not for one moment does He forget you, or your name. When Jesus came to live on earth to show us what God is like, He had lots of friends—and He called them each by name. And even after He had been crucified on the cruel Cross, and God had brought Him back to life again in the dewy garden where His tomb was, on the Easter morning, He still remembered. There was a woman who went to that dewy garden in the early morning. She was sad; she wanted to find out what had happened to Jesus. And as she stood weeping, someone asked her, 'Why weepest thou?' And she said, 'Because they have taken away my Lord, and I know not where they have lain Him.' And when she had said that, she turned and stood face to face with someone she thought was the gardener. And He asked her, 'Woman, why weepest thou?' She told him the same, but it wasn't the gardener—it was Jesus. And He said to her just one word, her name—Mary! He hadn't forgotten. And when she heard Him say her name she was full of joy. Of course, He hadn't forgotten. How could He, because He is like God. God never forgets your name—nor you. Don't forget Him, will you?

He gives you lots of reminders—the sunshine and beauty of the world; His air to breathe, and His water to swim in; and His Church; and His Book, and so many other things. All the time He is saying to you, as to the little blue-eyed flower, FORGET-ME-NOT!

The New Song

ALL UP and down the valley the children were filled with excitement. This was the night of the year when they were allowed to stay up late. Presently they would pull on their thick hoods, and each take a little lantern and go to the church. For this was Christmas Eve, and a happy time for children. Already the stars shone crisp and clear overhead, and a great stillness lay on the countryside.

They could not know that in a poor peasant home away up on one of the slopes that night a little child had been born. A message had come down the valley to their young pastor, Joseph Mohr, to come up and bless it. Pastor Mohr had been sitting quietly reading over to himself for the hundredth time the age-old story of the first Christmas, and the little babe that had been born. And as he laid aside his book, and pulled on his cloak and took a stout stick, to go up to the humble home on the high mountainside, it seemed to him a greater wonder than all other wonders.

In the poor home he found the mother and the father and babe, just as long ago the shepherds had found Mary and Joseph and the Babe in the manger. It was different, this high Austrian village on the mountainside, but it seemed that God was very close to their homes and their little children that night. As he picked his careful way down again by the light of his lantern, the stars shone overhead and a great stillness lay around. And a song began to sing in his heart. Over and over the words came, over and over. And almost before he knew it, he had come to the door of his own little cottage.

It was too soon yet to go to the church.

Pastor Mohr slipped off his cloak, and put out his lantern. Then reaching for a sheet of paper, he set down the words that had come.

Late that night he gave the words he had written to his good friend Franz Gruber, the village schoolmaster and organist. Franz was charmed with them:

Silent night, holy night—
All is calm, all is bright,
Round yon Virgin Mother and Child;
Holy infant, so tender and mild,
Sleep in heavenly peace—
Sleep in heavenly peace.

Early on that Christmas morning, 1818, Franz Gruber came eagerly to seek out the Pastor. He had made a lovely tune that exactly matched the lovely words. And presently, the two men sang it together:

Silent night, holy night—
Darkness flies, all is light,
Shepherds hear the angels sing,
Alleluia! Hail the King!
Christ the Saviour is born,
Christ the Saviour is born.

By degrees the song they made together became the favourite Christmas song.

It chanced that of all the sweet voices of the children living in the valley and on the high slopes, the sweetest were those of the Strasser children. Caroline, Joseph, Andreas, and Amali loved to sing. They sang at home, and in the market of Leipzig. Every year they went to Leipzig to help Mother and Father at the stall where they sold the chamois gloves they had made.

A merry crowd pressed through the market, but there were times when the crowd was happy to linger. That was when Caroline, Joseph, Andreas, and Amali sang.

One year, the children sang a song that nobody had heard before, but it went on singing in the hearts of those who heard it.

When they had finished, an old gentleman stepped forward and spoke to them. His name was Mr Pohlenz. And he was the Director-General of Music in the Kingdom of Saxony. He told them that he had been charmed with their singing. Then he put his hand deep down into his pocket, and brought out four tickets. His concerts were famous, and were held in the ancient and beautiful Guild House of the drapers of Leipzig.

The children looked at their tickets excitedly. But when the time came at last, and they went into the great hall full of fine gentlemen, and ladies with rustling silk gowns, they were shy.

And they were even more shy when, at the end of the concert, Mr Pohlenz rose to his feet. 'In this great company,' said he, 'there are four children with the sweetest voices in Austria.' They sang their favourite song, then other songs they knew, and last of all, their favourite song again:

Silent night, holy night,
Guiding star lend thy light,
See the Eastern wise men bring
Gifts and homage to our King!
Christ the Saviour is born,
Christ the Saviour is born.

When they stopped the fine ladies and gentlemen were very still and reverent—then great applause filled the place. A messenger came forward to Mr Pohlenz: 'Their Majesties the King and Queen of Saxony,' he said, 'desire to receive the children.'

'Where did you learn that lovely Christmas song?' they asked.

'We learned it at home, Your Majesties,' the children replied simply. 'Many girls and boys on the high slopes, and in the valleys where we live, now sing it at Christmas.'

Said the King: 'It would give us great happiness if you would come and sing it in our church at Christmas.'

And on a crisp, clear Christmas Eve, in 1832, to everyone's delight the children stood in the Royal Chapel of the Saxon Court and sang the lovely song with the lovely words. And since that night long ago all the world has learned to sing their song:

Silent night, holy night,
Wondrous stars, lend thy light;
With the angels let us sing
Alleluias to our King!
Christ the Saviour is born,
Christ the Saviour is born.

Miles and Miles Away

ONCE UPON a time there was a little pedlar called John Chapman. He lived during the reign of King Henry the Seventh. Pedlar John wore a large floppy hat, and carried a pack full of things to sell. He lived at Swaffham, and he wandered far and wide, with his little dog beside him, selling the things in his pack.

One night Pedlar John had a dream. And the next night the same one, and again the third night. And it was so strange that he felt it must mean something special.

He dreamt that someone told him that if he went to London Bridge something good would happen. So Pedlar John sat down on the grassy roadside and thought and thought about it. He felt the heaviness of his pack, and he looked at his little dog beside him. London Bridge was over a hundred miles away.

But with his little dog, and his pack full of things to sell, he set off. It took him a long time, and he became a little lonely so far from home. But at last he got there.

He was much impressed by the sights that he saw—the great houses and the booths. And he walked across London Bridge just as the dream had told him, with his half-empty pack on his back, and his little dog beside him. Then he walked back again, and back again. And all day he walked backwards and forwards, waiting for the good thing to happen to him so far from home.

Towards evening, a shopkeeper on the Bridge could hold his curiosity no longer. He came out and talked to him, and asked what he was waiting for.

Pedlar John told him about his dream. 'It was a good dream,' he said, 'and I dreamed it three times over. And it said that if I came to London Bridge something good would happen to me. So I came. It was a long way, but I came.'

The shopkeeper laughed at him for a simple fellow. 'There's nothing in dreams,' he said. 'Why, I had a dream myself. I dreamt of a place called Swaffham, and my dream said that if I went there I should meet a pedlar with a little dog, and a plot of ground, with an apple tree, and under the apple tree I should find a pot of gold buried deep. That was my dream. But who takes notice of dreams?'

But Pedlar John did. He hastened home again to Swaffham as fast as he could. He was tired and footsore when he arrived, but, forgetting his tiredness, he began straightway to dig under his tree. And there, to his surprise, he found an old mug full of coins. On the side of the mug were printed some Latin words, which he couldn't make out. But he kept the old mug, and one day a clever man came by, and he told Pedlar John what the words meant. He said they meant, 'Under me is another twice as big.'

When Pedlar John heard that, his heart bounded with excitement. And when the clever man had gone out of sight, he began to dig again.

This time, he found a bigger mug than ever. And his eyes shone with joy. He told no one of his good fortune, but he said to himself, 'There are things right here under my nose more precious than on London Bridge. I was a foolish fellow to think I had to travel so far to find good things.'

And none guessed Pedlar John's good fortune, until

one day the Parish Church of Swaffham was badly in need of repair. And to the surprise of everybody, the little pedlar gave two hundred golden sovereigns. That was a very great deal to give. And it filled the church-people with such joy as they finished the re-building of their beautiful church, that they got a clever wood-carver to carve the figures of Pedlar John and his little dog on the ends of the seats in the Church.

In the Book of Proverbs is a text about people like Pedlar John. It says: *The eyes of a fool are in the ends of the earth* (Proverbs 17[24]). It means that foolish people still go on looking in faraway places for rich things like happiness and joy and beauty, when all the time they are round about them at home where they are growing up day by day.

Little Black Sue

THE RESTAURANT was full. People sat sipping their coffee. But the restaurant man seemed restless. He kept looking towards the door, and then at his watch. 'It's the middle of the morning,' he said, 'and our regular customer hasn't come yet.'

Who was this regular customer? A shopper with a bulging purse? A duchess with a shining silk frock? No!

But she had never disappointed the restaurant man before.

It seemed a long time back to that first morning when down the Folkestone street she had trit-trotted softly and seriously.

At a corner she had suddenly stopped, and said to herself, 'Ah, a nice smell! I must find out, if I can, where this comes from.'

Her four little feet moved quicker, and her joy in the lovely smell grew stronger. At last, she stopped before an unknown door. 'This must be it,' she said; 'but it doesn't look like a house.'

It wasn't a house—it was a restaurant. Inside were tables, all of them full that sunny morning. Some of those who sat at them saw Sue, the little black terrier, come in. But humans are not always clever. 'She has lost her master,' said one. 'I expect she belongs to someone in here,' said another. But, of course, they were wrong, quite wrong.

She wanted only to find the man who owned the lovely new smell. Soon she came to where he worked in a great white apron. She stood by the leg of his table, her little black nose held high. Said he, 'Hello, my little friend! What do you want?' And because he had understanding rare among humans, he guessed what a little dog with a black nose would want at that hour of the morning.

He set down beside his tall table a handful of tasty scraps.

'Not only the lovely smell,' thought Sue to herself, 'but scraps and a kind heart too.' And from that moment Sue and the restaurant man were friends.

Next morning, as promptly, and with more assurance, Sue found her way there again.

'Back again, are you?' said her new friend in the great white apron. 'I haven't forgotten you.' And he called his assistants to see her go off with a bone. It looked almost too big for Sue to carry, but she managed somehow.

And next morning she was there again.

So it was every morning, until the restaurant man christened her with the name she was known by ever after—'our regular customer'.

But now the restaurant man was worried. She hadn't come. At first he began to doubt the old clock, tick-tocking away on the wall. Better doubt the clock than that she wouldn't come. Slowly the minute hand of the old clock crept on—five minutes past, twenty minutes past, one whole hour! And night came—and one whole day had gone by. And there was no Sue.

'I hope she is all right,' said the restaurant man.

'Never fear,' said his assistants. 'She will be all right. She'll come tomorrow.'

But when the morrow came, there was still no Sue. And the next morning came, and the next and the next.

At last the restaurant man could bear it no longer. Without a word, he took up a large paper and spread it out. Then from a secret hiding-place he brought out some sweet scraps. With a few quick movements he wrapped them up. Next minute he had snatched off his white apron. 'If anyone calls,' said he to his assistants, 'tell them I've gone to call upon a regular customer.'

The people who sat at the restaurant tables, chatting and sipping their coffee, were surprised. They'd never seen the restaurant man with his apron off before. But then they'd never seen him paying a social call on a regular customer.

From door to door he went, hugging his parcel. Many times he knocked, until at last he came to a special little shop of an antique dealer. There were beautiful things in his window—valuable things, and treasurable. But the restaurant man had no interest in such. He had only one question to ask: 'Does a regular customer of mine live here—a little lady who dresses in black?'

'Yes,' said the antique man. 'As a matter of fact, she does. How nice of you to call. I am sure she will be pleased to see you. No; she hasn't been out for a day or two.'

Then he led the restaurant man with his parcel through to the back of the shop. Next minute Sue was looking up into his face, and the two friends were reconciled.

And it wasn't very long before Sue was back again at the restaurant, paying her usual call—and bringing seven little new customers with her.

The Dream that Came True

ONE DAY a little girl walked to and fro in a dream. It was a day-time dream—one of the most wonderful of all.

Her name was Mary Jones. She lived with her father and mother in a little Welsh village. It was a lovely place in which to live. Above towered a great mountain, with lovely colours changing from blue to purple.

But Mary's father and mother were poor. A bench of wood, two or three stools, a cupboard, a kitchen table, and a loom were all they had. Most precious of all was the loom, because Father was a weaver. From early morning till late at night he worked. It was pleasant work, but poorly paid, and luxuries were unknown in Mary's home.

But there was one night in the week that Mary always looked forward to. It was the night when people gathered from far and near to hear the stories of the Bible. They were all friendly people, and Mary was allowed to go to carry the lantern. It was very dark going to and from the meeting.

Coming home one night, Mary said: 'Mother, why can't we have a Bible of our own? Then we could read the stories for ourselves.'

'Bibles are very scarce, child,' said her mother. 'And besides, they cost a great deal.'

'I expect it is easier for you to wait,' said Mary, 'because you have waited so long, but sometimes it seems as if I can't wait a minute longer.'

Neither Mary nor her mother said any more that night, but next day Mary thought about it as she fed her hens and gathered the eggs, and as she looked after her hive of bees.

Then one afternoon when her father and mother were busy, and she was sewing on a patch, there came a little knock at the door.

Next minute, in stepped Mrs Evans, a neighbour who went to the meeting with them.

'Good day to you,' said Mrs Evans. 'How is everyone —and Mr Jones's chest?'

Soon they fell to talking about the stories they had heard at the meeting.

'I only wish I could give Mary a bit of schooling,' said Mr Jones. 'She is eight years old, but what can we do?'

Mary looked up at her father, and her face lightened. 'Oh, if only I could learn,' she said. 'It's dreadful not to know how to read. I should like to read the Bible stories.'

'You forget, Mary, that we've no Bible,' said her mother.

But Mary never for one moment forgot.

'Yes; it is a great want in our country,' said Mrs Evans. 'Perhaps some day you will get your chance to learn. And,' she added kindly, 'when that day comes, you are welcome to come up and read my Bible as often as you like.'

'Oh, thank you,' said Mary. 'That is kind. It is only two miles up to your place.'

Mrs Evans rose to go. 'Dear me,' said she, 'I'm forgetting my errand. I came to get a dozen new-laid eggs.'

Mary counted out the eggs into Mrs Evans's basket.

And when she had gone she could think of nothing but the promise that one day she should read Mrs Evans's Bible.

Weeks went by and months went by. Then Mary's father came home very excited. 'A school is going to open in a village two miles away,' said he. 'A master has been found, and in a few weeks all will be ready.'

'Now I shall learn to read!' said Mary as she danced round the little kitchen. 'Now I shall learn to read!'

Weeks and months went by, and at last the happy day came when Mary made her way up to Mrs Evans's house. It was a quaint old house, but Mary's heart sang for joy. Soon she was reading the great Book.

But once a week was so seldom. 'I must have a Bible of my own,' she kept saying to herself. 'I must! I must!'

At once she started to do jobs for the neighbours, and her father made her a little money-box to put up on the shelf. Sometimes she earned a farthing, sometimes a halfpenny; and it seemed the box would never get full.

When kind Mrs Evans heard about Mary's money-box, she gave her a cock and two hens. 'When the hens lay, you must sell the eggs,' said Mrs Evans.

So Mary saved and saved. For six whole years she saved, until at last she had enough to buy a Bible of her own.

But where was she to get it? The village shops sold only sugar and tea and boots. There were no shops that sold Bibles. Then her schoolmaster told her of a minister, a Rev. Thomas Charles, who could sometimes get Bibles for people. But he lived twenty-five miles away. Twenty-five miles was a long way.

But early one morning Mary left home, carrying her little money-box, her lunch and her shoes—for she feared they might get dusty if she wore them.

All that day she walked on and on. It was almost dark when she got to Bala, her journey's end. But she sought out the house of a good friend, and in the morning they both made their way to Mr Charles's home.

'There is a light in his window,' said the good friend, 'so he must be up. We will knock.' And they knocked, and the Rev. Mr Charles came to the door.

He was surprised to see anyone so early, but Mary told him her story.

Mr Charles had only one Bible left, and that was half-promised to someone else. But soon his mind was made up.

The other person should be asked to wait.

And half an hour later Mary was on her way home again, her heart so full of happiness that she forgot to count the miles.

Her dream had come true. And late that night she came to her own little home under the mountains.

And it was the beginning of dreams coming true for very many other people. For two years later the Rev. Mr Charles went down to London, and told some of his friends there of little Mary Jones and her Bible. 'What a pity it is,' they said, 'that this Book is so hard to get. Let us start a Society to print Bibles and make them cheap so that even the poorest child can have one—and let us print so many that they can be had without going so long a walk.'

And they started the wonderful British and Foreign Bible Society, which has gone on printing Bibles ever since. And it all started with little Mary Jones and her dream.

A Pocketful of Gold

ONCE THERE was a dear, absent-minded old man. He had a smiling face and a hole in his pocket. Once it was a very small hole. But the dear, absent-minded old man had forgotten how a hole can grow.

One day, out on his walk, he came upon a friend with some wonderful seeds.

'Put these in your pocket,' said he, 'and you will never lack gold. They are called by a long and difficult name—nasturtiums. It matters little that you remember the name, so long as you remember to plant them in May.'

And the dear, absent-minded old man was delighted.

The days went by, and the nights went by. And always he took his walks abroad. He visited old Jamie who was sick. He told stories to the boys and girls when they tired of their games. He walked to the house of Tony, who was crippled. And one day he knocked at old Shepherd John's door.

Old Shepherd John had been used to the sweet air of the hills. And now he was shut indoors. He loved a visit from the dear, absent-minded old man.

But one day when he called, there was no answer. He knocked once, he knocked twice. The sun was pleasant upon the world, and he knocked again. Old Shepherd John had grown deaf, and more deaf. He knocked a fourth time. And still there was no stir in the little house. But a window stood open. And in a trice he decided to pay his visit that way. 'What a surprise he will get,' said he, 'to see a man with a pocketful of gold coming in at his window.'

But a surprise waited for the dear, absent-minded old man himself. Once in, and happily seated, he told old Shepherd John about his seeds. 'I promised to plant them in May. But I will give you a little of my gold,' said he with a smile, 'for a rich man is always the better for sharing his gold.' But when he put his hand in his pocket, there was not a single nasturtium seed there—not one.

'Now where is my gold?' asked he. 'Where is my gold?'

'Your gold is in your heart, I guess,' said old Shepherd John, 'for no man in this parish is more kind and true.'

And the dear, absent-minded old man went upon his way. 'It is little that I can do,' said he, 'save visit a few folk and cheer them with a tale and a smile. I did mean to plant a corner of my garden with gold this May. And now I have a hole in my pocket. Ah, me!'

When May came at last, all over the parish little crinkled seeds began to root. Some found soft soil by the path of old Jamie. Others put down little roots in the shade of a great tree where many a time the children gathered for stories. Some began near the porch of Tony, crippled and lonely. Some, oddly enough, grew by the open window of old Shepherd John.

And when they broke forth into golden flowers, the parish was transformed. And people who thought they were poor suddenly thanked God they had gold in plenty. And because it is *more blessed to give than receive* (Acts 20[35]), none was happier of heart, or richer, than the dear, absent-minded old man.

The Little Music-maker

ONCE THERE was a merry miller who had a son. And that son had a son. And that son had two sons. And one of those two sons had also two sons.

And every one of those sons was musical. But the most musical of them all was little Johann Sebastian Bach. While he was still a very little boy he loved nothing so much as to listen to music.

But sad to say, when he was still a little boy of ten, his father and mother died. That was a sad time. And little Johann Sebastian Bach wondered what was going to happen to him. What did happen was that he went to live with a big, older brother. But the sad days of little Johann Sebastian Bach were not over, for the big, elder brother was not kind to him. He let him live in his house, but he was not kind to him. He sent him to school, but he was not kind to him. And many and many and many a time big tears welled up in his eyes. But always there was the music of the clavichord and the harpsichord to comfort his sad heart. And it was sweet, soft, tinkly music, for this was a long time ago. The clavichord and harpsichord were the grandmother and grandfather of pianos. They were very much smaller, and could only make very small silvery, tinkly sounds of music. But to little Johann Sebastian Bach they seemed the sweetest sounds in the world. And when he felt sad and lonely in his big, unkind brother's house, he used to draw his stool up to the clavichord or the harpsichord and play until he forgot all about the sadness in his heart.

His fingers would not always do what he wanted them to do, and he had to go over his music lots and lots of times, but bit by bit the little silvery, tinkly notes came sweeter and sweeter.

And a day came when little Johann Sebastian Bach had played all the music he knew, and there was no more for him to play. It was like being hungry with no food left to eat, or thirsty and no streams of water left in the world to drink.

Then he learned that there was a book—a book of beautiful music—away up in a high cupboard. But the cupboard was locked. The more little Johann Sebastian Bach thought about it, the more he wanted it. He knew already too much of the unkindness of his big brother to ask his help, so he had to think out another plan. For a long time there seemed no way of getting the beautiful music, but at last he thought of a way. He tried making his hand very small. He knew he could not open the strong lock. His hope was that he could screw up his hand very small, and when he was alone, squeeze it through the little lattice decorations on the front of the cupboard.

But what could he do with the beautiful music once he got it out? That was the next hard thing to decide. But little Johann Sebastian Bach loved music so much that he was ready to overcome any obstacle in his way. He told himself he would copy out the beautiful music into a book of his own. Then he would be able to learn it, and after he had tried it over lots and lots of times, play it for himself. It might take a little boy a long time to copy it out. But little Johann Sebastian loved his music so much that he meant to overcome that obstacle too. And he did. He waited for a long, long time, until the tiny, sharp, sickle moon that looked through his window at night became a fat, round moon, with a soft, white, pure light that made everything in his room clear as clear. And then little Johann Sebastian Bach knew that the time had come to conquer the biggest obstacle of all.

When the house was all still and quiet, he climbed from his bed, and, putting a wrap around him, went tiptoe to where the high cupboard was. It was a brave thing to do—but anyone who is to overcome difficulties has to be brave. And he got the beautiful music out through the tiny lattice decorations in the front of the cupboard. His heart beat pit-a-pat, pit-a-pat with excitement, but soon he stilled his heart and steadied his hand. Then he copied out the beautiful music. He couldn't do it all in one night. It took a long time. But at last, his hard task was finished by the light of the big fat moon that looked through his window.

And how happy he was!

But he was happiest of all when he began to write music for himself. And when it was played, it was far, far more beautiful than even the music he had copied out in the moonlight. And soon people all over the world were thanking God with all their hearts for the music and the courage of Johann Sebastian Bach.

Hurry Up and Choose!

IT WAS a lovely day. The soft wind carried the happy voices from the green. Little Freddie Charrington and his friends were playing a favourite game. Two of them had selected two things beautiful and precious. Now, one by one, the children passed under their clasped hands. And all the while they sang:

Oranges and Lemons,
Say the bells of St Clement's;
You owe me five farthings,
And when will you pay me?

Then down came the hands, and the end of the song:

Chip, chop, chip, chop,
Last man's head off!

The 'last man' had then to choose between the two things beautiful and precious. A golden brooch or a diamond ring. And all the time that he hesitated, his friends cried, 'Hurry up and choose!'

But the time came when Freddie was a man, and had to give up 'Oranges and Lemons' on the green. Still the cry of his playmates rang in his ears: 'Hurry up and choose!'

It was harder to choose now. Freddie had the chance to be a very rich man. One of the richest breweries in England belonged to Freddie's family. But always there echoed in his heart the cry of his old playmates.

One night when he was coming home he passed a lighted public-house in one of London's back streets. It was in a very poor part of the great city. As Freddie came towards it, a mother and her two little children stood at the swinging door, begging their father to come home. It was late, and the father was drunk and quarrelsome, and in a trice he lifted up his great fist and knocked down his wife.

Freddie Charrington saw it all happen, and he was very troubled—more than ever, when he chanced to look up and saw that the letters over the door spelled out his own name: C.H.A.R.R.I.N.G.T.O.N. It was one of his family's drinking-houses.

As he continued on his way, the cry of his old playmates rang in his ears: 'Hurry up and choose!' And he made his choice.

His father, when Freddie told him, was very, very angry. 'But I cannot make any other choice,' said Freddie. 'That great fellow who knocked down his wife has knocked me out of the brewery business.'

Freddie moved from his comfortable home of ease and wealth, and went to live instead amongst the poor of Stepney, in the East End of London. There were lots of people who had been made poor by the breweries and the drinking-houses that made his own family rich.

But soon Freddie knew that he was rich himself—in the most lasting way—in the love and kindness of the poor people. And he stayed amongst them, and did all he could to help them.

Then came a day that he would never forget. His old father, who had been so angry with him, was ill, and he sent for him, and said to him a very wonderful thing. 'Fred,' he said, 'you are right!' And then he borrowed some words that Jesus had used a long time ago: *You have chosen the better part, that shall never be taken away.*

And though Freddie was very, very glad to hear his father say it, he had known in his heart all the time that it was so.

Number Six

THE PRIDE of Bennie Locke was lovely to see. His great engine, 'Number Six,' was a very special engine. And he and his mate polished her and cared for her lovingly.

Always, after her hard climb over the mountains, as she stood in the station hissing with steam like a great dragon, boys and girls came to admire her. After dark, she looked even bigger—her great lamp carving a pathway through the darkness, her wheels shiny as silver where the light fell on them.

For fifty-seven years Bennie had driven an engine, and there wasn't a single black mark against him. But then every time Bennie climbed up into his great cab, he took off his cap for a moment, and silently asked God to make him a good engine-driver—to keep his eyes open, and his wits about him, and do his job well.

One day 'Number Six' was delayed a whole twenty-five minutes in getting away. And as Bennie climbed into his cab, he added a little bit to his usual prayer. He prayed, as usual, to be helped to keep his eyes open and his wits about him. Then he added: 'Lord, help me to bring her in on time!'

The first stage of the journey was a stiff climb, and 'Number Six' couldn't gain a single lost minute, no matter how she tried. But when they got to the top of the Pocono Mountains, Bennie knew there was a chance.

It seemed to Bennie and to those who travelled with them that day, that 'Number Six' just flew down the mountains. It was grand. 'I just kept her steady,' said Bennie, 'and let her go.'

Soon, working together, they had made up five minutes, then fifteen, then twenty. And last of all, the whole twenty-five minutes. And Bennie and 'Number Six' pulled into the terminus, with a rush of steam, right dead on time!

As Bennie rubbed his hands clean and made ready to step down, he heard a tap-tap on his cab. 'Who is that?' he asked. Then he looked out, and to his surprise it was the President of the railroad. And he was looking up at Bennie with a smile, and saying: 'A good run, sir! A very good run!' And Bennie smiled back, for he was very proud to hear such words.

But later, when Bennie's friends asked him about his good run, he owned that there was just one thing that he would like even more.

'And what is that, Bennie?' they asked.

For a moment Bennie did not speak. And then he said: 'It is just this: that when I make my life's last run, and pull in at the end, I should like to hear God say, "*A good run, sir! A very good run!*" '

Bennie was a happy man. He loved his great 'Number Six', and drove her well. And he loved every day of his life that God gave him, and lived it well. It wasn't hard for him to remember a text in the New Testament: *Whatsoever ye do, do all to the glory of God* (1 Corinthians 10^{31}).

All Secretly under His Tunic

LONG, LONG ago there lived a merchant with a fear at his heart. He went about the country and found himself sometimes in the company of strange men.

Now, it chanced that a smith who owed him a debt fell upon evil days. He was also an armourer, and when he was unable to discharge his debt he begged the merchant to take from him goods. And the merchant did so. He chose a fine suit of chain armour.

'Yes, indeed,' said the smith, happy to be relieved of his debt, 'this is the very thing for you. You are a rich man, and these are evil times. There is no telling when a rogue may thrust his sword into your heart. Tell no man, but wear this all secretly under your tunic.'

And the merchant, well pleased, took it home under cover of darkness.

Next morning, before any was astir, he fitted on his new armour. At first it hindered his movement, but now he knew that he would be able to look into the face of any stranger, and say, 'Ah! You may be a robber. For all I know, you might carry a short, sharp sword of mischief. But, my man, you cannot get at my heart.'

Soon his wife came down to bid him a tender good morning, but suddenly she drew back with a cry: 'What is this under your tunic? What strange thing is this?'

'It is no strange thing,' answered her lord the merchant, as casually as possible. 'It is a shirt of chain armour. If any rogue thinks to get at my heart, I am prepared, and he shall be mightily surprised.'

But his lady wife had no words of praise for his wisdom. Instead, a great fear gripped at her heart. 'But is it so dangerous on the highways?' she asked, scarcely able to bear his answer. And from that moment she had no peace of mind. As soon as he was out of her sight, she began to fear for his safety. And when he did not return for months, she was certain that evil had befallen him. And the lustre departed from her eyes, and she grew strained and lined.

One day as her lord the merchant was on his travels, and sat at wine, a jocular friend poked him. 'But what is this plaguey thing under your tunic?' he asked.

'Oh, it is nothing,' replied he. 'Only a coat of chain armour. These are evil days, and there are rogues about.'

No more was said whilst he was present, but when he

had gone his friends whispered about the ugly secret that must lie in his private life.

'What else,' they asked, 'could make a man so cautious? He must have a secret enemy. He must have done someone a grievous wrong.' And from that moment their trust in his goodness was gone.

One dark night, returning from a distant city, the merchant found himself in a wild place. His purse was more than usually fat, and the clouds rushed across the moon.

'This,' said he to himself, his heart thumping under his tunic, 'is the very place where one might expect to find rogues.' As it happened no rogues sheltered there, but as he looked right and left, and upward at the clouds flying across the face of the moon, somehow he missed his step and fell into a swiftly flowing river. Down he sank. And the waters carried him quickly past a shadowed bank, and beneath an arched bridge, down and down.

He tried to swim, but with the weight of his armour that was quite impossible. He tried to put his foot on to the bottom, but it was too deep. After a time, when he had swallowed much water, a strong hand took hold of him and dragged him up the steep bank. He began at once to babble: 'If it hadn't been . . . for my coat of armour . . . I could have swum. . . . If it hadn't been . . . for my coat of armour. . . . If it hadn't been . . .'

His rescuers turned him over roughly, tugged at his clothes and moved his arms and legs.

When next he was able to speak, he was all but stripped. And in a heap on the river-side lay his coat of chain armour. As he staggered to his feet, and saw it lying there, he seemed to be seeing it for what it was for the first time. Next minute there was a mighty splash.

'What is that?' exclaimed his rescuers.

'That,' said the merchant, surprised at his own courage, 'that is my worst enemy.' And his suit of chain armour sank to the bottom of the river. 'I see now,' said he, 'that a man has no enemy like the fears of his own heart.'

∽

Sally's Dream

SALLY SNUGGLED down into her little bed. 'By this time tomorrow,' she murmured, 'we shall be there.' It seemed that the holidays would never come. First it was two whole weeks, then one whole week, and then only one more day.

They were going to the seaside, to stay at a big boarding-house. It was kept by a kind landlady whom Sally had never seen. But from all that Daddy had told her, it seemed certain they would soon be friends. At first, Sally had to be told what kind of a lady a landlady was—that she did all sorts of nice things to make people's holidays comfortable and happy, and only collected a few pounds from them at the end of the time.

Excited, Sally snuggled down for her last sleep in her own little bed.

But before the sun came up again over the hills and peeped into her window, she dreamed a dream. At first it hardly seemed like a dream, it was so real. It was all about the craziest boarding-house in the world, and the craziest landlady. Instead of welcoming people for their holidays, she seemed scarcely to care whether they stayed or not. And instead of collecting a few pounds from them at the end of the week, she had a way all her own. She came and talked to Sally and her father and mother when they had only been in her house two minutes. 'My charges,' she said, 'are fourpence for every step you go up, and a penny for every step you go down. And threepence every time you sit down; and sixpence every time you get up.'

'But how shall we remember it all?' thought Sally.

'Then,' added the crazy landlady, not a bit changed in her plans because Sally wasn't good at her sums, 'there's heat from the fire. That's a ha'penny a minute. And looking out of the window is a penny each pane. And opening a window for air is sixpence a time. And sunshine is more than that—a pound a gleam. Now these are the rules of my house; and if you don't like them, you must go.'

What else she said Sally couldn't remember, for next minute she was rubbing her eyes, and the sun was coming up over the hills. And she was in her own little bed. But nothing could rub out altogether her dream of the crazy landlady.

'Daddy has never told me,' she said, 'but surely she won't be like that. And her boarding-house . . .' But Sally switched on to something happier, and jumped out of bed. 'How wonderful it is that God hasn't made the world like that! Just supposing we had to pay a hundred pounds every time the sun came up over the hills! And that wouldn't be too much. And a thousand pounds for a starry night!' But Sally couldn't think of such a world—she wasn't good enough at her sums. 'But then nobody in the world would be good enough at sums for all that,' said she. 'How much would it be for a friend? And how much for clear eyes to see? Oh, dear,' sighed Sally, 'it would be impossible to add it all up. Nobody in the world would be good enough at sums for all that.'

So Sally started to dress, and Mother called in her morning voice that always sounded so happy: 'Sally! Sally! Get up, my sleepy head. The holidays have come!'

And a little verse that Sally had learned came dancing into her mind. It said:

When I can pay the sunshine
For shining in my face,
Or recompense the violet
For her exceeding grace;
When money helps the moonbeams
To wax awhile or wane;
When silver lures the summer;
When bank-notes bribe the rain;
When for a salary, the stars
Shine clearer and more true,
That very day I'll surely pay,
You, dear—for being you!

Sally saw in that moment that God's world was full of good things that no one could pay for. A good Daddy. A good Mummy. A good church. A good school. And now holidays at the seaside. They were all gifts of His love that God had given in His wonderful way—*all things to enjoy* (1 Timothy 6^{17}). And Sally danced merrily down the stairs to breakfast.